DAVID ANGUS

The Life and Adventures of a Victorian Railway Engineer

DAVID ANGUS

The Life and Adventures of a Victorian Railway Engineer

by

Craig Mair

THE STRONG OAK PRESS

ISBN 1-871048-12-5

Published by THE STRONG OAK PRESS
              Spa Books Ltd
              PO Box 47
              Stevenage
              Herts SG2 8UH

The publishers acknowledge subsidy from the Scottish Arts Council towards the publication of this volume.

Typesetting by Litho Link Limited, Welshpool, Powys
Printed in Great Britain by The Camelot Press, Southampton

DAVID ANGUS

To the descendants of David and Mary Angus who, though scattered across the world, are held together as a family by their memory.

Also by Craig Mair:

A Time in Turkey
A Star for Seamen: The Stevenson Family of Engineers
The Lighthouse Boy
Britain at War 1914-1919
Mercat Cross and Tolbooth

CONTENTS

    24 pages of illustrations and maps
    appear after page 84.

Author's Note

David Angus's life was both exciting and productive. As an engineer in wild places he was often caught up in adventures, and as a builder of railways, bridges and harbours he had the chance to leave a worthwhile mark on the world – something given to comparatively few people.

Like hundreds of other Victorian engineers, he did the work, solved the problems or faced the dangers, but his employers carved their names on the stones or plaques erected to mark his achievements. History will record, for example, that D. and T. Stevenson built the Ailsa Craig lighthouse, that the firm of Sir George B. Bruce and White surveyed the Otavi Railway across the Namibian Desert, or that Prebble and Ware Ltd. built the railway from Buenos Aires to Rosario; this account sets the record straight. At the same time it lights a candle to all those other nameless forgotten Victorian engineering heroes who were sent by their employers to live and work and often die in remote places around the world.

David Angus's story has never been told before; this has been written almost entirely from surviving family records. A large collection of letters, diaries, field notebooks, reports, drawings, plans, maps and photographs has been collected by David Angus's daughters Louie and Helen, and deposited at the Scottish National Library in Edinburgh. Many more documents are still in the family's possession but these are less concerned with David Angus's business and engineering affairs.

It is with gratitude that I thank Patrick Cadell for his help at the Scottish National Library, the descendants of the Stevenson family for the use of their family engineering records, and especially Mrs. Louie Proctor for her great help in researching through her father's papers. Mrs. Proctor also made available her own unpublished account of the Angus family, the transcript of a BBC broadcast about her mother's adventures in South America, and also her extensive collection of useful photographs (from which all the illustrations in this book have been taken). In addition she provided me with a marvellous fund of family stories and recollections, some of them about the colourful exploits of other Wilsons and Anguses which sadly could only be hinted at here. Nevertheless I am very appreciative of her hard work, kindness, hospitality and trust.

Letters and diaries have been extensively quoted, but David Angus's spelling and grammar were not always perfect – extracts have been given just as he wrote them, errors and all. Place names have also been left unchanged. In a few cases where hurried pencil scribbles in notebooks have been difficult to decipher, I have simply done my best. I would be interested to hear from any readers who similarly tackle the originals and who feel that I have misinterpreted David Angus's writing. The letters from Brazil and Damaraland are especially interesting and plentiful, but were written in such outlandish places and under such difficult conditions that they are especially difficult to read. But then, the rewards for perseverance are greater.

Finally, thanks to my wife Anne for her help and patience with the typescript, and to Janice Gilland for checking and re-typing the text.

Bridge of Allan   Craig Mair
Stirlingshire

Introduction

From the scientist John J. Buchanan to Sir Donald Currie, October 7th, 1893.

'Dear Sir Donald,
The bearer of this is my friend Mr. David Angus, C.E. whom I have known for many years. Mr. Angus has had charge of the construction of important railways in South America, and he has made an admirable survey of some land in the Argentine Republic which belonged to my father. Quite recently he has carried the survey of a railway from the sea to the interior of Damaraland in South Africa.

In connection with this, and from my long personal acquaintance with him, I have great pleasure in introducing him to you.

(signed) John J. Buchanan'

David Angus (1855-1926) was born the son of a Scottish schoolmaster, was raised in Scotland, and became an engineer. Though given an early training by the famous Stevenson firm of lighthouse builders (through whom he became great friends with Robert Louis Stevenson), he eventually made his own mark as a railway surveyor and builder in South America. At a time when railway fever was sweeping the American continent, he surveyed or built remarkable railways in Brazil, Argentina, Uruguay, Chile and Paraguay, through mountains, jungles, deserts and swamps.

It was a life of great danger and adventure, enough to provide his friend Arthur Conan Doyle with the background for his book *The Lost Continent*. David Angus lived through many revolutions when he saw men killed before him, had snipers on the roof of his own house in Paraguay, and once had part of his ear shot off through a train window in Chile. He entertained several presidents in his home, survived numerous earthquakes or tidal waves, explored for oil in the foothills of the Andes Mountains, and lived through murder attempts and bandit hold-ups. Moreover, throughout these adventures he was accompanied by his Scottish wife and a family of ultimately thirteen children, who went with him from country to country. Indeed their story of adventures and resiliance overshadows even that of his railways.

Though living mostly abroad, David Angus remained always a strong Scot, a remarkable humanitarian, a powerful leader of men and yet also a strong and loving father. This is his colourful story, written mostly from family papers and diaries and the memories of his surviving children. The Angus family today feel that their father was little different from hundreds of other unsung engineers of Victorian times who lived and worked in far-flung places, but what emerges from his story is the picture of a remarkable and courageous man.

Chapter One

CHILDHOOD 1855-1874

Many notable Scottish engineers have sprung from the most unlikely origins. Thomas Telford, who built roads and bridges, was the son of a border shepherd. The family of James Watt, the steam engineer, were trading merchants. John Rennie, the eminent civil engineer, was born on a farm, and the steamship pioneer Henry Bell was born in a mill. David Angus made his name as a railway engineer but his background was just as unlikely, for his father was a village schoolmaster. Remarkably, from an Angus family of six sons and a daughter, five boys including David went to work as engineers of one kind or another, while the sixth became an accountant and eventually an American millionaire. And yet the beginnings seemed all so unpromising.

By 1800 the Anguses had lived for centuries in Strathearn and the quiet lower valley of the River Tay in Perthshire. Mostly they had married locally, which kept them generally in the one district, but it was a fertile enough land in which to make a living. Like many Scottish families they managed to trace some sort of descent from Rob Roy MacGregor (David's father and several others had MacGregor for a middle name, as if to confirm this assertion). Through one of the wives they also went back to a Welsh bow-man taken prisoner at the Battle of Bannockburn in 1314, but there were Anguses fighting on the side of Robert the Bruce too.

As a family they were, are still are, proud of their deep Scottish roots. David Angus himself used to croon his children to sleep with the gathering song of Clan MacGregor and other Scottish songs, even in the wilds of South America. There are plenty of tales from the Angus family past, of battles and legends and memorable characters, and a few of how they simply survived the ravages of Scotland's war-scarred history. Nowadays the family still retells the story of Clan MacNeish (for MacNeish and Angus derive from the same ancient Gaelic name, it seems). They tell how in 1612 Smooth John MacNab and his men carried a boat over the hills from Loch Tay and slaughtered almost all the men of the MacNeish clan on an island in Loch Earn. These were times when a fragile family could disappear for ever in a moment of blood, soon to be forgotten itself in history.

By the nineteenth century the struggle for survival was, of course, less urgent for the last battles were long ago. The scourge of disease still lurked to take its toll of children but the Angus family were good at producing plenty of healthy robust boys who could keep the name strong. They were now living mostly as tenant farmers or traders around the modest seaport of Newburgh on the south bank of the Tay estuary. As cattle farmers they seem to have supplied milk to the nearby city of Perth, but they also owned several cargo sloops which plied between Dundee and ports as far afield as Wick and London, sometimes also sailing back up the river to Newburgh or Perth. The Anguses seem to have been reasonably well off by the start of the nineteenth century, but it seems from stories in the family that they were still not above a bit of smuggling at times as well. 'The barrels they carried in their sloops would be unlikely to contain milk' is how they coyly explain it today. At any rate they were never caught and duly became respectable local citizens.

David Angus's grandfather, one of these Jekyll and Hyde citizens of Newburgh, fathered four children – three sons and a daughter, of whom William, the future father of David Angus the engineer, was the youngest. These Anguses were typical of many Scottish families of the time. Above all they were serious and devout Protestants, perhaps more determined than some, for after the Disruption of 1843 when the Church of Scotland split over its beliefs, they followed the more extreme Free Church. In common with most other Calvinist folk, they also believed in the enduring values of a good education, hard work, sober living and a strict but at least well-meaning family discipline – beliefs which have shaped many a successful Scot over the years.

In keeping with these ideas, William Angus followed his two older brothers to Perth Academy, easily the best local school for boys, but unlike David and Henry who subsequently became blacksmiths, William discovered a more academic inclination and eventually progressed in 1845 to the Free Church Normal School at Edinburgh. At this time, just after the Disruption, the Free Church was busy establishing its own schools all over Scotland, and this college, with others in Glasgow and

Aberdeen, was founded to train Free Church school teachers.

Here in Edinburgh, away from the confines of home life, William met Betsy and Anne Stewart, who were on the same teacher training course and who came from Dundee. Being all three of them from the Firth of Tay in a strange city may have brought them together more often than usual, but at any rate William soon fell in love with Betsy. Marriage was, of course, out of the question until William could find a job, but perhaps encouraged by this thought he became an excellent student. During his training William seems to have done spells in actual schools, for a testimonial of 1847 from St. David's School in Dundee states that he taught there for several months during the illness of the regular teacher and that his work was much appreciated. Another from the Free Church School at Torphichen in West Lothian adds that they would have liked to have kept him on after a time which he spent there. Then in 1848 William qualified at last as a proper schoolmaster and an inspector noted that: 'William Angus is personally well qualified for the office of teacher and secures considerable attention from a class without undue noise. His expositions are fluent and simple and his lessons well arranged, addressed to the children's understandings and easily remembered and his mode of examination is both judicious and animated.'

That same year he was appointed to the Free Church School at Dalreoch on the western outskirts of Dumbarton, and in 1849 he secured his Teacher's Parchment. Each year after this an inspection was made and an entry was added to this parchment praising or criticising the progress and running of the school. William's parchment shows him to have been a fine schoolmaster.

Having found himself satisfactory employment, William married Betsy Stewart in 1850 and she now joined him at Dalreoch. A year later James was born, followed by Isobel in 1853. Then on July 29th, 1855 David Angus was born, like his older brother and sister, in the school-house at Dalreoch. The school offered William and Betsy a living but it cannot have been much. Free Church schools could not offer even the salary of a normal parish school for they were supported by a smaller part of the population. Despite this Betsy does not appear to have used her training as a teacher so perhaps William was able to earn enough for them all by himself. At any rate the couple lived for ten years at Dalreoch and young David spent his first few years there.

At this time Dumbarton was a growing town with new shipyards and engineworks springing up all along the River Leven which separated Dalreoch from Dumbarton. The *Cutty Sark*, that famous sailing clipper, was built here in the 1860's, and railways already connected the town with Glasgow. More were built just as David was born, and in that decade the population rose from around 5,000 to over 8,000 for Dumbarton was undoubtedly prospering. Dalreoch became a focus for many of the town's bigger houses and some of these children may even have attended William's school, but despite all this the family moved out in 1860. Why they moved is not clear – there was intermittent and sometimes very serious trouble between local Protestants and immigrant Irish catholic navvies employed on nearby construction schemes, and this may have worried the Anguses. Perhaps, and more probably, they simply needed a bigger income, for another son was born in 1858. Whatever the reason, early in 1860 the Anguses and their four children left Dalreoch and the bustle of Dumbarton, and moved to the Presbyterian School at Inse near Wigan in Lancashire. In June 1860 the local Protestant Minister seems to have inspected the school, for he added a separate testimonial to William's teaching parchment. It ran: 'Having had many opportunities of visiting the Presbyterian Grammar School here taught by Mr. Angus, and of inspecting the material, *animus et modus operandi* of his work, I have great pleasure in expressing my conviction of his thorough ability and efficiency as a Teacher and my high esteem for himself as a man. (Signed) Thomas Dalton, Minister, Wigan. June 20th 1860.' In just a few months, William had clearly established himself as a good teacher in this new place.

Then for some unknown reason William Angus simply disappeared. Some years later he returned again, but no-one ever explained to young David why his father had temporarily vanished. To her dying day, Betsy never told her children, and when William did finally reappear the matter was never mentioned in front of the family. However, two theories persist in the Angus family today. One feeling is that William had a row and simply walked out on his wife. Betsy was undoubtedly quite a nag, with a tom-boy nature and a set of very strong views which she was not afraid to stand up for at a time when other Victorian wives 'knew their place'. William also had a fiery temper, and yet it would have been out of character for the religious-minded father simply to abandon his family (though it might explain Betsy's reluctance to talk of the episode later). The alternative theory is that William may have been ill – perhaps a nervous breakdown or possibly the dreaded tuberculosis. This terrible, but sadly common, illness was frequently hushed up by middle-class Victorians, especially in front of the children.

Whatever the reason, William's disappearance certainly had its effect on young David. In 1860 Betsy was pregnant again and George, her fifth child, was born in the schoolhouse at Wigan. Abandoned by her husband and with five children all under ten years old to support, Betsy did the sensible thing and moved back to Scotland. Her sister Anne Stewart, still unmarried, was now teaching at a small Dame School in her home town of Dundee, so Betsy moved in with her children and began teaching with Anne. Even so, the strain of coping with her children while also working to maintain them was considerable. Fortunately at this moment the Angus luck changed. An opportunity arose for David to go as a boarder to Cauvin's Hospital in Edinburgh.

This charity institution, bequeathed by a French teacher in Edinburgh, was opened in 1833 specifically to provide 'relief, maintenance, clothing and education' for the sons of impoverished but respectable teachers or honest farmers (failing which, printers and booksellers). Amusingly, Cauvin added in his will that the schoolmasters had to be male and teachers of 'proper subjects', for he would have nothing to do with 'tutors of music, drawing, fencing, dancing etc.'.

The school was pleasantly situated by Duddingston Loch in the lea of Arthur's Seat, a prominent Edinburgh hill. It normally housed around twenty boys, who started when they were about eight or nine years old. David seems to have entered the school in 1863 when he was eight. Soon his letters home showed that he was loving the place, fitting in easily with the other boys and evidently enjoying the caring atmosphere for which Cauvin's was well known. The curriculum, which must have been quite challenging for such a young boy, included English, Reading, Writing, Arithmetic, Religious Education (how Scottish schools stressed the four R's!) plus Book-keeping Latin, French, Mathematics, some Geography, Natural Philosophy, Chemistry, Botany, Music and Drawing. It seems that younger boys concentrated first on the basic subjects and progressed to more difficult things later on, but there is no doubt that Cauvin's Hospital was a good school. David was certainly fortunate to have been sent there, for during its existence many excellent pupils progressed on to varied distinguished careers.

A photograph of David has survived from this period. It shows a rather timid and skinny eight year old boy with fine black hair and nervous eyes, but it is misleading. Several of his letters home have survived and they are more accurate. Written in a steadily improving beautiful copper-plate hand, they reveal a happy boy, not at all miserable at being seperated from his family in Dundee but still concerned and thinking of them. Cauvin's seems to have injected a balanced sensible out-look on life, and not a little self-reliance, for such a young boy. This was a letter written in January, 1865, when David was nine:

'Dear Mother,
I received James' kind letter and the pictures in it. I was happy to hear that you are all quite well. I wish all friends a very happy New Year. I enjoyed myself exceedingly at the happy season. We had a football match on Christmas Day and a party at night on New Year's Evening. We had splendid fun. We had theatricals and four of us acted the parts of Christy's Minstrels. I took a part and got on very well. Mr. Brockley showed us the Magic Lantern. He has lots of new slides and it was first rate. So much for our amusements. Our first quarter's marks have been added up. I must tell you my places. We have not been marked either in Writing or Mental Arithmetic this quarter until we are properly classified.

English .... 6th   Dictation .... 7th   Geography .. 7th
Latin .... 6th   Arithmetic ... 1st   French 5th

I am determined to do better next quarter. I give kindest love to all friends. I remain, Your affect. son,

David Angus'

Of course, many a boarding school letter home has been written under the censorial eye of a strict housemaster, but David's letters convey the undeniable impression of a lad at peace with his lot. He writes of liking the teachers and of his Saturday interests, but he always asks of home and often lists his three brothers and sister in his best wishes. Cauvin's Hospital was obviously a good place for David during this time of his father's absence.

In mid-1864 William Angus seems to have reappeared, however, and was now appointed to the Free Church School at Findhorn on the Moray Firth. A letter from David dated September 1864 says 'when you go to Findhorn please write me', and the first Findhorn entry to William's teacher's parchment was made in November 1864. As a result, Betsy and her four children in Dundee now moved north to Findhorn, and in 1866 David also left Cauvin's Hospital in Edinburgh to attend his father's school instead. The family was now completely reunited, mostly without apparent recrimination or hard feelings. William seems to have been a concerned and caring parent, doing his best now to make up for lost time with his family. Later two more boys were born, both in the schoolhouse at Findhorn, probably in 1868 and 1870. They were John and Duncan and brought the family to its final total of five boys and Isabella the only girl.

William was back and the family was together again, but the break had had its effect and there were undoubtedly favourites and loyalties among the Anguses. George, for example, who had been born at Wigan just when his father disappeared, was certainly his mother's favourite – indeed to such an extent that the others seem to have been rather jealous, referring to him for years after as 'none-such' in some of their letters to each other. The boys also had a strong love for their aunt Anne Stewart, who had helped Betsy care for them all. In much later life when she was an invalid in a bath chair, the boys looked after her and even when times were very hard David always sent money to his elderly aunt.

Although the children, especially David, seem to have re-established a fair relationship with their father, Betsy always remained the favourite parent. Photographs show a rather serious woman in typical voluminous Victorian skirts, but she must have had a soft spot for her children for in one letter from

Cauvin's David felt bold enough to write '. . . when you write send me a fairy tale book' – the very idea of demanding from a Victorian parent! Later in life all the sons called daughters after Betsy, but not one christened a son William. David also called one of his daughters Anne, after his aunt in Dundee. 'All that we are we owe to our mother,' wrote David, perhaps unfairly, to his brothers when Betsy eventually died, but he was expressing a general family feeling.

Findhorn was a small place of under 1,000 people. A natural harbour and two stone jetties provided a safe anchorage and at this time plenty of vessels still used the port. Many of the local people were sea traders or fishermen working boats out in the Moray Firth. As a result the burgh had grown in the haphazard way that many fishing villages do. Little thatched houses mostly without gardens stepped straight onto narrow twisting cobble lanes, most of which led eventually to the harbour. Inside, most homes had just two rooms, with stone-flagged floors, box-beds and an inevitable open kitchen range. The Angus schoolhouse may have been a little bigger, but it must still have been a crowded home.

There was a local parish school which educated a majority of the Findhorn children, but William Angus seems to have been busy enough at the Free Church School. It was evidently quite a rough place when he arrived and clearly needed the firm hand of a new master to restore order. In his first year at Findhorn, for example, William learned that one particular day was always kept as a school holiday, but to his horror he later discovered that this was simply used by the boys in his school to walk along the beach towards Lossiemouth, where they met boys from another school for a battle with stones. That year a boy was actually killed and William stopped the custom.

Being a schoolmaster (and not even the village dominie at that) in such a distant village as Findhorn must have been an academically frustrating life. Doubtless William unearthed an occasional 'lad o' pairts' but that was not often. To some extent David's father found fulfillment in writing essays on Scottish history and folklore. These were even published in newspapers like the *Dundee Telegraph* and the *Elgin Courant,* which must have given him some satisfaction, but he also produced a lot of poetry which his descendants nowadays correctly describe as 'long and tedious screeds on history and religion' with only an occasional 'tolerable lyric'. Fortunately he generally used 'Beth' or 'Beta' as a pseudonym!

William Angus seems to have been quite an able mathematician, however, and his children and other pupils became particularly good at this subject. David was already quite capable when he left Cauvin's Hospital and he now steadily improved. Later in life this mathematical ability proved to be one of his greatest hallmarks as an engineer – a skill which he owed at least in part to his father. Many future employers commented on David's mathematical accuracy in testimonials.

William put his own numeracy to good use by also taking evening classes in mathematics. Seamen especially attended, for they needed navigation certificates to qualify as ships' masters or mates at Findhorn. A good many ships' captains eventually owed their tickets to William's evening classes, and doubtless the extra income also helped the Anguses. They certainly needed it, for the family was not well off. The children frequently had oatmeal porridge for breakfast, dinner and tea and in summer they usually ran about barefoot. David was sometimes dressed in a kilt, not so much because he was Scottish but because trousers would have worn through sooner. It is curious how the Scots have always respected and admired their schoolmasters and yet paid them so little.

In 1865 David's older brother James ran away from home at the age of fourteen. All the Angus boys were developing into extremely independant lads, with surprisingly defiant and strong-willed natures for the Victorian age in which they lived. James perhaps objected to the reintroduction of a proper discipline, now that his father was back from that mysterious absence, so he just ran off. The boy did not get far, for he was recognised at Peterhead by a skipper from Findhorn, and was brought home again by this man. However the episode resulted in James being sent to Dundee, where he lived with his aunt Anne and attended Dundee High School. (James must also have been a good mathematician, for he subsequently entered a general office, became an accountant, and died a real-estate millionaire in San Francisco.) James's escapade also had an effect upon David, for it marked a change in William's plans for his sons. In 1870 when David was fifteen years old he was also sent to Dundee High School, and other younger brothers followed later.

Among the papers from this time in David's life there survives a curious document written by a 'Professor Fowler', probably a travelling fairground fortune-teller. This man wrote an interesting 'character reference' for the boy, which ran as follows:

'David Angus has good circulation of the blood is strong (sic). Good health. Good appetite. Good humoured. No veneration, is full of Fun and Pleasantry. Mischievous. Careless. Fond of teasing. Speaks his mind too freely. Lets another praise him. Love of praise. Small Self Esteem. Great power of mind. Planning Scientific. Good memory. Artistic. Mathematical. Kind. Social. Generous. Should be an Engineer. Love of Mother. Good memory of Poetry. Obedient if told and advised. Disobedient if forced and compelled. Knows Right from Wrong. Benevolent. Speaks a great deal. 26th March, 1870.'

He may only have been a travelling showman but Professor Fowler could not have summarised the boy better. All the facets of personality and character formed in his early life, and which would shape his adult nature, were plain to see in this fifteen year old boy.

Shortly after this David moved to his aunt's house and enrolled at Dundee High School, at fees of £1 per term. At the same time he was also apprenticed to the Dundee Burgh Architect, a local civil engineer called Robert Blackadder. This seems to have been the first clear pointer to David's future except for Professor Fowler's uncanny recommendation. Just why William decided (if indeed it was William) that his son should turn to engineering is unknown. James, after all, was currently training to be an accountant, and there was little sign of an industrial bent in the family. Betsy's father ran a quarry in Dundee but it is too vague a link. William's two brothers became blacksmiths, and both then joined the railway when it reached Perth in the 1860's — however Henry then distinguished himself by becoming the first person to be killed by a train at Perth, so this venture into a more mechanical world was hardly a great encouragement either. Engineering and construction were certainly in the air everywhere in Victorian

Scotland. There was plenty of work and the pay was good, but nothing more specific than a general mathematical ability seems to have pushed David in this direction.

Whatever the reason, he now began work with Blackadder while attending technical drawing and mathematics classes at the High School in what today would be called a 'sandwich course' or 'day release'. It was seemingly quite a normal thing at that time and lots of other boys did the same. A later testimonial from Blackadder indicates the training and experience which David was given by his master:

> 'Mr. David Angus served his apprenticeship with me, and learned the usual routine business of a provincial Civil Engineer's office. He had constant practice in surveying and levelling for works, such as Land Drainage, Sanitary and Sewage Drains, Improvements of Water Courses, etc. etc. He also had to locate, Survey and Level two short railways to Brickworks. He was very steady, intelligent and careful with his work.
>
> (signed) R. Blackadder.'

Many a man's future has been influenced by the habits engrained into him by early training and teaching. David's personality may have been unusually opinionated and defiant, but Blackadder seems to have grafted onto this a real interest in workmanship and good planning. This was important, for an engineer must often accept the dictates of higher masters and yet fulfil the work to high standards no matter how little his heart may be in that particular project.

Blackadder's training may even have helped David come closer to his father, for letters from this period suggest a fairly easy and improving relationship with home. William's letters especially convey the assurance of a man unashamed of his past, while David seems to have turned quite willingly to his father for advice, as in this typical letter from 1872:

> '. . . Tomorrow is your (seventeenth) birthday, and you are rapidly getting to be a *man* now. A few years hence and you will be your own master and as you learn to comport yourself now, so you will turn out later. I trust that you

sometimes think seriously of this, and that you will strive to be what your God and mine desire you to be – a man – in the highest sense of that expression. You are to be allowed to join the Volunteers, but do not take any steps in the matter until you come home as I should like that you should have a good select company with which to join. I was a volunteer myself once and would be again if the opportunity arose but I know some companies are neither a credit to themselves or to the Corps. I would like the company you enter should be reputable, otherwise it would be no good to you. I enclose a few stamps for you to show that we remember your birthday. We are all well and speak of you often . . .'

No record survives to show if David ever did join the Volunteers, but by the time he first went to South America in 1882 he could certainly ride and shoot.

Photographs of this time also show David growing into a fine big strapping man. All the Anguses had a tendency to be tall and broad, and David followed in the typical family mould. He certainly would have made an impressive volunteer as a later teenager. By now he had an open, honest sort of face, with hair combed back and alert, clear eyes of a self-assured young man. When employers later met David at interviews these character-istics must have conveyed a good first impression. He also posed easily in front of any camera, and spoke with assurance among friends – and there were many friends, for he was good company. If you did not mind his monopolising manner he could be friendly, garrulous, witty and full of fun, and very easy to socialise with. It was a feature of his adult life that he seemed to collect good friends, from all ranks of life, very readily.

In 1874 David completed his courses at Dundee High School. In so doing he won the Baxter Silver Medal for Mathematics, and a Baxter Scholarship in Engineering to Edinburgh University, which must have pleased his school-master father very much. David seems to have had a natural love or gift for these subjects, but he also had a steady, accurate approach; the feeling of a job well done seems to have given him great satisfaction. Later, in South America, this blended with the pleasures of adventure and excitement which his work also involved.

That same summer David also left Robert Blackadder's office, with the following complimentary report:

'Mr. David Angus completed a four year apprenticeship in my office on the 23rd May last, and I have great satisfaction in giving him a first-class testimonial for the manner in which he has attended to his duties. He has had varied practice in measuring and designing architectural plans, surveying and levelling of engineering plans; and I have found him careful and accurate.'

It was typical of many testimonials which David was to receive all through life as he moved from one railway project to another in South America.

That year things also began to improve for the rest of the Angus family, for William was now appointed to a better teaching post in Glasgow. Here he was made Headmaster of a group of buildings generally known as the London Road Schools, but which seem to have centred on the Sister Street Public School. This involved authority over quite a large staff, with an appropriate rise in salary – when he died some years later he was earning over £30 per month and the Anguses were living in Langside, a typical middle-class part of Glasgow. For those Angus children still living at home the days of bare feet and porridge morning, noon and night were past.

David seems to have moved with his parents to Glasgow during the summer of 1874, for classes at Edinburgh University did not begin until September. However, since his Baxter Scholarship was evidently not enough to live on, he meanwhile found work as the advising engineer at Dunoon Water Works and started earning the money to see him through college. No clue remains as to the nature of his job, but it was probably occasional for he stayed on in the post even after term began at the university. A testimonial dated April, 1875 states:

'I have pleasure in certifying that I have known Mr. David Angus for upwards of a year. During most of that time he acted as Engineer for Messrs. Band, at Dunoon Water-works, and I can bear favourable testimony to the able and careful manner in which he discharged his duties.

(signed) James Tait.'

Then, at last, David began classes at Edinburgh University and he moved to lodgings in the capital city. A whole new world of interesting people and eventually even marriage, was about to open up for him.

Chapter Two

THE YOUNG MAN 1874-1882

In the autumn of 1874 David moved to Edinburgh, where he found digs in Marchmont Street, a respectable part of the city not too far from the university. Most of the college clustered round a fine Adam quadrangle in the older part of the city, so David would have crossed the Meadows, a pleasant open park, on his way to classes each day. In September there is often no more agreeable place in the city, better known for its windy streets and the crowded houses and smoky chimneys of the Old Town.

David studied mathematics and engineering, but for an Arts degree as was still the habit then. Under the guiding hand of Professor Fleeming Jenkin he worked well for two years, gaining good marks but no prizes. Later the professor wrote that '. . . David Ángus's attendance was excellent and he did the work of the class in a creditable manner.'

Inevitably the genial young man soon found many friends at university. David was a particularly keen chess player – an interest which perhaps arose from his love of mathematics – and he belonged to the university chess club. He seems to have had little interest in organised team games or even in the Scottish obsession for golf, but he did find exercise, at least in winter, through skating. A thriving club flourished in Edinburgh, where there are several pleasant small lochs. Unfortunately these did not always freeze over each winter, but when the opportunity arose the members would assemble to glide elegantly in complicated figures 'reminiscent of a corps de ballet' as one skater wrote. David spent many hours joining in this fun, particularly on Duddingston Loch which he knew so well from his days at Cauvin's Hospital close by.

All through university, however, David remained short of money, for the Baxter Scholarship was not enough to provide for fees, books, food and lodgings. His parents may have helped, now that David's father had a better post in Glasgow, but no record of any assistance has survived in family papers and it is more likely, and in character, that David tried to fend for himself. To begin with he remained in the part-time post as engineer to the Dunoon Water Works, but it was not an easy job to fulfil properly. Travelling from Edinburgh to Dunoon involved a train to Glasgow, a change of station for the train to Greenock, and then a ferry across the Firth of Clyde to Dunoon itself, so in spring 1875 he gave up the post.

By great good fortune David found work instead as a junior employee with the Edinburgh civil engineering firm of David and Thomas Stevenson. He now began part-time work with them in a 'sandwich course' similar to that which he had followed earlier with Blackadder in Dundee.

No record survives to explain how the Stevenson men came to hear of David. They certainly knew Professor Fleeming Jenkin very well, and he may have recommended David as a promising student. The Stevensons and Professor Jenkin also skated in the same club to which David belonged, and they may have met socially to begin with. Or perhaps it was through David Stevenson's two sons, David and Charles. At this point they were both at Edinburgh University studying science and engineering under the same Professor Jenkin. They were of similar age to David Angus – one graduated in 1875 and the other in 1877 – so that they may even have attended the same classes. Almost certainly they at least knew each other, and it is possible that the Stevenson boys mentioned David Angus to their father. At any rate, he was given a part-time junior post in the office.

To be taken on by the Stevensons was certainly a scoop for David, and says much for the personality and character he conveyed to others. The Stevensons had been noted lighthouse engineers in Scotland for almost a century when David joined them, and they now enjoyed a long-established and justly-famed reputation for great skill and engineering enterprise. David and Thomas Stevenson were the second generation to work from the family office in George Street; their father Robert had first won prestige by erecting the famous Bell Rock lighthouse on a reef in the North Sea in 1811, and then their older brother Alan had repeated the feat on the storm-lashed Skerryvore Rock in the Atlantic in 1843. When David joined them they had recently finished building yet another famous lighthouse on the Dhu Heartach rock, also far out in the Atlantic. In fact the Stevensons had built (or would go on to build) every single lighthouse in Scotland, reaching a total of nearly one hundred by the 1930's in a dynasty which eventually spanned five generations.*

Although best known for their spectacular lighthouses, so often perched on inaccessible cliffs or half-submerged rocks, the firm was also noted for a host of other engineering works. As civil engineers they surveyed, designed and built roads, harbours, bridges and railways all over Britain. They also repaired dams and canals and advised on sewerage schemes, river reclamation, street lighting and reservoir construction in a wide range of work ideally varied to give any new employee a thorough introduction to many engineering skills and problems.

David soon found working for the Stevensons a gruelling experience however. They believed strongly in keeping the nose to the grindstone, as Robert Stevenson had done to his sons when they trained in the same office. As a result, there was an established family tradition of relentless hard work, and David was now given endless tracings to copy, calculations to make, and diagrams and plans to prepare. The Stevensons also demanded very high quality work from their employees and insisted that even when unsupervised they should privately set themselves high standards. Fortunately David revelled in the work and his drawings and calculations were completed with a beauty and remarkable accuracy which continued to be an Angus hallmark all his life. David may have arrived in Edinburgh with a mathematical ability, but the Stevensons certainly refined it, polishing it with a commitment to high standards and high personal integrity.

Although perhaps he did not realise it to begin with, David also had an additional handicap to overcome when he joined the Stevensons in 1875. Thomas Stevenson's only child was Robert Louis Stevenson, later destined to become a great author, but who at this point was still only a young man of 25. Thomas very much wanted his son to follow in his engineering footsteps, but fate was against him. Illness and a fitful education had left R.L.S. disenchanted with the discipline and planning required of an engineer, whereas travel and a lively

---

*See Craig Mair 'A Star for Seamen: The Stevenson Family of Engineers' John Murray, 1978.

imagination had seeded the germ that would one day make him such a fine story-teller. So while David Stevenson's two sons now studied to follow in the firm, Thomas's son had refused to do likewise in a memorable confrontation in 1871. The empty chair still stood in the office where R.L.S. had briefly toiled under his father's eye until that rebellion.

In 1875 R.L.S. passed the final examinations for his law degree at Edinburgh University, but he was never called to the bar and in any case he had no real interest in law, having studied it as an alternative profession only to placate his father's fury at not becoming an engineer. Thomas Stevenson dominated the firm now, more by his gruff determined personality than by seniority – David Stevenson was actually three years older, but was too mild-mannered to resist his brother's dictatorship, for he understood Tom's bitterness and disappointment. So now, while R.L.S. went on to find fame as an author, David Angus occupied the vacant chair in the office. This really was the 'hot seat'! It must have been a difficult time both for Thomas and the new employee.

In the summer of 1876 David's scholarship from Dundee High School expired, and he left Edinburgh University having completed only two years' study. He said later that he could not afford to take his degree because of the fees and extra expenses, but it is probable that he was finding the practical work with the Stevensons more useful anyway. In later life he always recommended practical training and workshop experience over academic study. Soon after leaving the university David was appointed a full-time assistant with the Stevensons, who had evidently been much impressed by his careful mathematical accuracy, and for the next six years he remained with the firm.

To begin with much of the work was very menial, for in the days before carbon paper and photocopies, junior employees in offices all over the world had to duplicate maps, reports and letters by hand. Gradually, however, David was given more responsibility and was sent off on projects all over Scotland to assist with measurements and surveys.

This was the very hey-day of the Stevenson firm, for they were now erecting lighthouses in Japan and New Zealand as well as round the Scottish coast. These also had to be inspected regularly, and even David was sometimes sent off on a coastal steamer or government revenue cutter to the more remote Scottish lights. In addition, as consultant engineers the Stevensons were always busy with an amazing variety of smaller schemes which kept all the office juniors constantly at work.

Although often preoccupied with the more grandiose work of lighthouses, Thomas Stevenson nevertheless kept a tight rein on his assistants no matter what less important task he had set them. Letters show that David could do very little without first notifying Thomas – fortunately the post in those days was noticeably quicker than today and a constant stream of letters flowed between David and his masters whenever the assistant was away on a project. One typical scheme for example, involved designing and building a sewage tank and settling ponds at Duns, in the Scottish borders. Although given charge of this work, David had nevertheless to inform Thomas of every step he proposed to take, as in this letter:

'Dear Sir,
I received your letter today authorising me to proceed with the work suggested. I have had an offer from a local joiner for the wooden trough of which you sent a sketch, and also for one as sketched (here a sketch) which is the usual style for conveying water here.

The offer is 2/– per yard for either, there being 69 yards required. I have asked the man who supplied the other pipes for the irrigation what he could supply the half 18″ pipes for and when he could have them on the ground. He is to give me an answer tomorrow. I have also written to Prestongrange Tile Works for an offer which I expect tomorrow.

I have arranged for six new men starting on Monday morning and think if other nine were engaged the work could be finished in three weeks (and so on).'

It is perhaps surprising that a business partner should have been so involved in the everyday trivia of small jobs, but this tight control undoubtedly made for first-class assistants. The same strict supervision can be seen in Thomas's letters to David. In one case, David was sent to the Mull of Kintyre to survey with Thomas for a new pier. Thomas was delayed, but that did not mean a day off for David:

> 'Dear Sir,
> I am to see Mr. Jamieson on Tuesday and will telegraph to you. In the meantime be sure to make full sections at the ferry so as to occupy your time.
> Yours faithfully, T. Stevenson.'

As a typical Victorian junior assistant, David also 'knew his place' in the office and always signed himself 'your obedient servant'. The Stevensons, however, varied in their replies from a formal 'yours faithfully' to 'yours truly' as David became more accepted. As time passed this became more common, though occasionally a 'yours faithfully' recorded mild irritation at some task delayed or not yet completed.

In 1867 Thomas Stevenson rented Swanston Cottage, a pleasant house which nestled in a fold of the Pentland Hills near Edinburgh. The original intention was to have a place with plenty of fresh air for R.L.S., who was often ill as a youth, but as the years passed and R.L.S. went on his way, Swanston became more of a weekend retreat for the family. Then as Stevenson letters to David came increasingly to end with 'yours very truly' he was also invited for Sundays at Swanston, and a deeper friendship began. Letters of instruction from the firm still conveyed a strong authoritarian tone, but privately David and the Stevensons clearly got on well.

There is no doubt that David was a likeable person. He was witty and fun-loving, an easy conversationalist and evidently a charmer in the nicest way to ladies, for over the years many were to comment on his engaging personality. Thomas Stevenson's wife Maggie particularly enjoyed dinners and bright conversation, and since fortune had given her a rather morose, introspective husband and a solitary, generally absent, rebellious son, she perhaps prompted the invitations to David. On the other hand, Thomas undoubtedly admired David's mathematical ability (Tom was a poor mathematician himself), and saw him as a young man of promise, perhaps even a protege.

While on these visits to Swanston David occasionally met R.L.S., and soon they became friends. During this period R.L.S. was often abroad, either recuperating from illness or simply travelling for fun – he made his travels with a donkey in the Cevennes in 1878, for example. As a result he was only occasionally in Scotland, but being only five years older than David and in a difficult domestic atmosphere, R.L.S. seems to have enjoyed meeting him again on each return.

Unfortunately no papers survive to tell more of this friendship, but in later life David used to tell his children how at Swanston, he and R.L.S. would sometimes go for evening strolls and become so engrossed in political discussion that they finished up walking all the way into Edinburgh. David used to recall that, at that time, R.L.S. had a theory that if all educated men married uneducated women, and if all uneducated men married educated women, the differences between the classes would be eliminated!

In 1879 R.L.S. met Fanny Osborne in France and subsequently travelled with her to America where they married. Knowing their son's theories about the classes, the parents worried terribly about what sort of woman Fanny might be. However when they met her the worry ceased. David was present at this first encounter, which seems to have been in the firm's office.

One task given to David as an assistant was to work on the construction of the lighthouse on Ailsa Craig, a humpy little island right in the path of ships sailing up the Firth of Clyde to Glasgow. It is perhaps a reflection of his admiration and friendship with the Stevensons that later in life David wanted to christen one of his daughters Anne Ines Louie Stewart Angus – the Louis was after R.L.S., but the initials would also have spelled AILSA. In the event David's wife drew the line at four names and the Stewart was omitted. As a compensation for this, perhaps, the child was usually called Louie, which she hated except that it forged a link between her father and somebody famous!

Despite the growing association with the Stevensons, David did not neglect his other friends. He maintained links with the university by attending balls there, and by skating with student companions. The Stevensons also skated, as did Professor

Jenkin, but David seems to have had his own circle of skating friends. These included James Ryan and James Drummond, both of whose families had returned to Scotland from Ceylon. The Drummonds had a flat on the corner of Marchmont Road and Warrender Park Road, close to David's lodgings. Another great friend was James Fairlie, who later became a noted architect, and there were many more, although it was with Ryan and Drummond that David seems to have been happiest. He sometimes came to tea with 'the three Drummond boys' and their mother, a young widow who seems to have delighted in his engaging personality. Through them David came to meet other young people.

One particular friend made through the Drummonds was a medical student called Arthur Doyle, whose father was the City Architect of Edinburgh. This student was soon to be better known as the writer Arthur Conan Doyle – indeed it was an Edinburgh doctor called Joseph Bell who was the prototype for Sherlock Holmes. Conan Doyle's friendship with David, though often interrupted for years by the nature of David's work in faraway places, survived until the two were in old age – and indeed beyond! When David died in 1926 two of his daughters went to see the elderly Conan Doyle for advice on selling their father's books. He was very friendly and helpful, but by that time he had become obsessed with spiritualism and thought that the two women had really come to have him contact David in the next world!

David probably first met Conan Doyle in the Drummond house, for the flat was quite a gathering place for parties and soirees. One of those who attended was an attractive young student called Mary Wilson, whose family lived in a flat downstairs. She later described this lively social life:

'Mrs. Drummond got up a little glee club amongst six families who lived near at hand, and once a week we met in different houses and practised lustily "O who will o'er the Downs with me?" and "Good morrow Mistress Fair" and other glees and madrigals. We never gave the public concerts we planned, nor did we carry our voices to cheer the sick wards of hospitals as we first intended, but we had many pleasant evenings together and enjoyed the company of other young people of both sexes. Two of Mrs.

Drummond's sisters often stayed with her, and they were both musical and very artistic. They painted their drawing-room walls with flowers and flowering shrubs from Ceylon and they painted pottery too and introduced us to ideas about interior decoration and the William Morris movement . . . Mrs. Drummond made everybody welcome and in spite of conventions and chaperones we had a very happy social life and Mrs. Drummond's glee club saw the start of many friendships and romances.'

The Wilsons came originally from Dunkeld where Mary's father had been the parish minister for years until his sudden death in 1877. Forced to vacate the manse, and with a large family to support, Mrs. Wilson moved to Edinburgh where she was friendly with several other sympathetic families.

'Poor mother,' wrote Mary Wilson later, 'left a widow at forty with eight children including a baby and only a tiny minister's pension. Mrs. Buchanan proved a real friend in need; she lived at 10 Murray Place just round the corner from our flat and she was very fond of my mother and liked to come and chat to her every afternoon. She was very deaf and mother was a good listener and they became great friends . . . Mrs. Buchanan was always helping us and giving us surprises. There would be a ring at the flat door and when it was opened a huge cheese would come rolling in; another time it might be a great tin of lard, round like a Christmas biscuit tin, or she might send in an extra chair or a whole set of curtains.' And so the family survived in genteel poverty.

Here the older children found their niches in life – Tom as a shipping clerk, Jessie as a music student in Germany, and Mary by first attending classes in mathematics, Latin and logic at Edinburgh University for a year and then by working locally as a part-time teacher.

During 1879 Mary was also very unwell. A sister had once died of consumption and the family feared the same would happen to Mary, so she was confined to the fourth floor flat and forbidden to go downstairs. Mrs. Wilson had several very kind and influential friends, however, all like Mrs. Buchanan, and one of these, Mrs. Murray of Stenton, who had known the family in Dunkeld, now came to give Mary piano lessons in the flat. Eventually Mary became a good pianist and passed the R.A.M.

Examinations. Then an uncle died and left all his money to the Wilson children so with this unexpected windfall the family moved house to Warrender Park Road and a flat below the Drummonds.

It was at one of the Drummond parties, carefully chaperoned but an acceptable mixed group nonetheless, that Mary first met David Angus. David already knew her brother Tom, another of the Drummond boys' friends, but the first encounter with his future wife seems to have been fairly casual. She was a pretty girl of twenty, with a bright personality that still shines vividly through her surviving letters, but at this moment thoughts of romance or marriage were still far from the minds of either of them as they concentrated on the careers they hoped to follow.

In 1880 Mary's sister Jessie returned from her music studies in Germany. By now she was a good pianist, despite the fact that she was born with two thumbs on one hand. The doctor cut one off but the other refused to grow so that she now played with a deformed hand. Nevertheless Mary and Jessie enjoyed the winter parties, and the flattering attentions of the young men who also attended. That Christmas at a dinner party given by Arthur Conan Doyle his mother asked David to escort Mary into dinner. It was probably the first time that Mary particularly noticed David from among the other young men of their group – Mrs. Doyle, at any rate, later got the credit for being the original match-maker.

In 1881 the two sisters were the first to leave this circle of friends when they decided to train properly as teachers. Their mother wanted them to attend the Church of Scotland College in Glasgow, as she had done, but the girls were determined to do something more adventurous and applied for a course at the Bishopsgate Central Ladies' Training College in London. When Mrs. Buchanan heard that Mary and Jessie proposed to spend their uncle's legacy on this training, she gave them each £100, and so the two went off to London where they eventually qualified a year later.

The sudden disappearance of Mary from the Drummond house may have stirred stronger feelings for her in David, and he now became noticeably more restless. Although kept very busy by the Stevenson firm, especially on the sewage scheme at Duns, he was now also looking round for a new post as an engineer in his own right – perhaps with the feeling that before he could marry he would need to have a better income.

Later in 1881 David was placed on the short list for a post with the Thames Conservancy Board. He travelled for the interview to London, where he also visited Mary and Jessie. He did not get the appointment, but he took the girls to the Crystal Palace and Madame Tussaud's, and then out to tea – much to the concern of Mary's landlady who felt that even these 'advanced women' training as teachers should nevertheless have had a chaperone! Later in the year David's friend James Fairlie also called on Mary in London, bringing with him a song called 'If this be vanity, who'd be wise?' Mary later wrote that 'it was all quite exciting', for obviously David was not the only young man who found her attractive. When Mary and David eventually became engaged, he could not understand why James Fairlie eased himself out of the circle of friends.

At the end of the year the two girls returned to Edinburgh, as Mary later described:

'The Christmas vacation while we were students was the gayest I ever remember. There were plenty of parties with games and singing and dancing. Jessie and I went to the University Ball (with David) and to concerts given by students. Best of all, perhaps, were the skating parties on Duddingston Loch. David Angus and I managed to get "lost" on the way back one night, and had a wonderful, unchaperoned walk home through Edinburgh.'

By now David had applied for several engineering posts without success. He was certainly busy enough with the Stevensons – he was often away on lighthouse inspection voyages, and in 1882 was also working on repairs to a dam near Forfar, and on the construction of the Ailsa Craig lighthouse. During a visit by R.L.S. the two men also carried out wind experiments for the Royal Society on the hills near Swanston Cottage, but David was certainly thinking now of a more independent career. As time passed and he failed to obtain a post in Britain, he turned more to overseas possibilities.

Undoubtedly the 1880's were a period of tremendous opportunity in engineering for anyone willing to travel and rough it a bit. A host of civil engineering schemes, ranging from railways in South Africa to irrigation canals in India, were under way all over the Empire, but Britain was also heavily engaged in work for other nations, in South America and the Far East especially. David decided that there had to be work for him somewhere overseas.

By now David was writing regularly to Mary in London. There was no hint of romance yet, but he told her of his ambitions and within the limits of social convention he paid her as much attention as possible. Clearly was now very keen on Mary, but she was just as keenly looking forward to teaching and did not particularly respond to David's flattering, but inconvenient, interest.

David, meanwhile, had heard of a railway survey about to begin in Brazil under the firm of Waring Brothers, who were now looking for engineers. The prospect of his winning a post were bright, but now he faced the agony of deciding whether to leave his feelings for Mary unresolved. On August 10th, 1882 he wrote to her:

'I had a letter from Messrs. Waring asking me if I would go to Brazil and if so, to send them a note of my experience, testimonials and salary I would go for. I wrote to several engineers who know me for testimonials, and also to Mr. McKerrow asking what salary I should go for, but I had a letter from Mr. Brumlees, his partner, saying he was on the continent and that I should send in my application at once, as the Engineers were wanted almost immediately. I sent up my application and testimonials at the end of last week; I asked £600 a year, but said I'd go for £400 and allowances to begin with. I am expecting their answer and believe there is no doubt about my appointment . . .'

The Stevensons gave David an excellent reference, which was vital, for there is no doubt that the firm was highly respected and could be trusted to produce good engineers. Their testimonial ran:

'We have much pleasure in certifying that Mr. David Angus has, during the last seven years, been in our employment and has given us perfect satisfaction. He is also strictly steady in his habits. He has during the term of his employment made many marine surveys and soundings for harbours and river improvements. He has also been engaged making working drawings of harbour, dock and lighthouse works. He is a good mathematician and calculator. He took the principal charge of some experiments on the force of the wind at different heights above the ground, which were carried out for the Meteorological Committee of the Royal Society of London, to Mr. Thomas Stevenson. Mr. Angus will always have our best wishes for his success.'

A few days later David was duly appointed as one of the engineers on the survey of a proposed line between the Brazilian seaport of Vittoria and the inland town of Natividade. He was told to be ready to sail from Southampton on September 24th. And yet the joy and excitement of securing a post at last were marred by the miseries of his pent-up feelings for Mary. At this moment, however, she returned from London, having qualified as a teacher. That same day David proposed to her, desperate to know where he stood with her before he left for Brazil.

Mary later recalled the moment:

'That very night David told me he cared for me and asked would I wait for him. He would come home for me as soon as this job in Brazil was over. I was overwhelmed and said I did not know him well enough, and that my training was only just finished and my career not yet begun. I could not give him an answer. I wasn't ready to think about marriage yet . . . My mother was very sympathetic. Her own marriage had meant the giving up of her career. She told David not to try to hurry me. This was partly, perhaps, because David had a reputation for being a bit of a radical, and my mother wanted him to settle down a bit too. (David actually called himself a Liberal, but his views were rather radical, whereas Mrs. Wilson and her friends were all firm Tories.) At the same time my mother felt that if David and I were engaged it might help him to keep straight among all the dangers and temptations in South

America. I didn't know what to do. It was a terribly exciting time with David coming in every evening, but I could not make up my mind and he was terribly anxious to have my promise before he went away to Brazil.'

Not surprisingly David's patience began to fray. Even Mary's mother and her brother Tom began to disapprove of her fluctuating feelings. In the end she was forbidden to see David again until she had an answer for him and meanwhile the Wilson family went off on holiday, taking Mary with them. This separation did the trick.

'Mother had taken a farmhouse at Dunkeld for August, and soon we would be away there, and in fact I did not see David again before we left. Each day I became more miserable, wanting to see him. Even the day we left, he did not turn up at the station to see us off as I had hoped he would. I was so desperate I wrote him a letter in the train, addressed to his lodgings in Marchmont Street, saying I must see him, and I got my little brother Archie to jump out and post it for me at Perth station. But there was no reply. Day after day passed and no answer came. I was nearly frantic, while the family called me sulky and teased me unmercifully. They said, with some reason, that my mopes were spoiling their holiday. I certainly could not appreciate the beautiful setting of that farm house at Fungarth.'

Then, after ten miserable days, a telegram arrived for Mary. It said 'Just got your letter arriving Saturday letter follows'. And soon the letter also came:

'My dearest Mary,
I have just got your letter and I can't tell you how much I was delighted to get it. I was afraid you had made up your mind and there was no hope for me, and I was nearly miserable as could be, but I feel the opposite extreme now. I went along to the Waverley (Station) at the time your train was to start, but had not the courage to go down to the platform, not knowing what my reception might be . . .

I am sorry I did not get your letter sooner. It was decreed that I should get *that letter,* for it was taken back and marked 'not found', then it came up again here with another and they were both marked 'out' (that is the door was closed) and it was not until the third time that it was taken in, so I think you'd better make up your mind that fate is on my side and don't let any doubts again disturb you in regard to your devoted lover, David Angus.'

Soon after, David arrived at Dunkeld and spent a week with the Wilsons. He and Mary walked together out over the hills and valleys and along the chain of lochs she had known in her childhood. Then Mary had to leave to take up a teaching post in London, and sadly David escorted her to the station, still waiting for her to accept his proposal. Just then an empty cab passed; David hailed it, they got in, and 'suddenly the flood-gates of my heart opened to him once and forever, and I knew he was mine and I never had another doubt', as Mary later recalled. They were engaged, but now David had to earn enough to let him marry.

For David there began a period of preparation for South America. From his mother there flowed an endless stream of advice, on not taking to drink, on keeping the Sabbath and avoiding the temptations of foreign women. David's father was more practical, and lent his son £200 with which to buy a tropical outfit and a set of surveying instruments.

Undoubtedly this was the right time for David to make a break from Scotland. He was a young man of twenty-seven, fit, brawny, strong and healthy. He was now a fine engineer – the Stevensons had seen to that – but he had also developed a deep sense of caring for his workers, perhaps a more important lesson also learned from the Stevensons. This was a typical Stevenson characteristic – ever since the days when Robert Stevenson had asked his men to work waist-deep in sea-water on the Bell Rock, the firm had looked after the workmen and their families with a sympathy and caring far beyond the norm of that time. They offered compensation for injuries and sympathetic leave of absence; they paid pensions to wives widowed by working accidents, and provided medical care and education even for their labourers. They insisted on good food for their workmen and ensured that even in remote places, the mail and the beer got through, for when men must undertake dangerous or remote engineering work, these are often the things which can forge a team between men and their leaders. The Stevensons did not need to teach this to their assistants – their actions spoke for themselves, and David learned well. In later years the concern for the men under his orders became an Angus characteristic as much as it typified the Stevensons.

There were more abstract things on David's side too. People liked him, and in South America where personal relations with local officials or suppliers or workmen could mean a venture's success or failure, this was a vital asset. And he was confident, almost cocky – in one interview he was asked how he would tackle certain difficulties and he ended his answer with '. . . and well on the whole I am a lucky man'. And he was.

Just before leaving Scotland he applied for associate membership of the Institute of Civil Engineers, one the basis of the work he had undertaken with the Stevensons. Later, when he was already in Brazil, this application was accepted, and two years later he was made a full member. David always regarded this membership as more important than a degree, for it acknowledged practical work and real achievements rather than academic abilities.

Some days before leaving Britain, David went to London to see Mary. He also found work surveying a tram line from Vauxhall Bridge to Kennington Oval, which he had to do very early each morning before the London traffic started. He was still working on this survey until the night before he left for Southampton, and in Brazil he bitterly regretted the lost time away from Mary, but it did help to repay the money his father had loaned him for his instruments. Finally Mary saw him off on a train from Waterloo Station and soon David boarded the S.S. *Trent*, miserable at leaving his fiancee but undoubtedly excited at the thought of working in Brazil.

Chapter Three

DAVID IN BRAZIL 1882-1884

The journey to Brazil took three weeks and was very tedious. David kept a journal each day and wrote to Mary with every mail, sending off a large number of letters to her from the ship's first stopping place at the Canary Islands. He must have been terribly keen to reach Brazil, for when the vessel finally arrived at Maceio, the first Brazilian port of call, his diary suddenly burst into enthusiastic description of local life.

'Macio (sic) looks well from the ship all surrounded by palm trees, but I believe it is very dirty. We are lying just inside a reef which runs all round the coast of Brazil . . . the boat mostly used by the natives here is a kind of raft called a fandango or catamaran. It is formed of four or five logs tied together and forming a space about three feet by twelve. Some of them have a lug-sail and mast, in others a man stands at the centre and uses an oar or paddle, about half a dozen strokes to one side and then on the other. Seen from a distance the man appears to be standing on the water. There are sometimes as many as six men on a fandango as well as luggage . . .' And so on, in an excited chatty style.

Soon the ship steamed on to Pernambuco, where David went briefly ashore and first observed the poverty which he would soon find so common in South America. From this first moment, he retained all through life a sympathy and compassion for the destitute natives of South America. As a young man he wrote of this first encounter:

'I met one small boy about Archie's age (eleven) dressed in a straw hat and carrying a bottle: I thought to myself, children's clothes do not cost much hereabouts. The next small boy I met had neither hat nor bottle and the full dress for children seems to be one dirty and remarkably short shirt; perhaps they have only one each and the other boys were having theirs washed! They didn't seem to mind whether it was on or off.'

From there, the *Trent* carried on to Bahia, where again David went ashore. The port was divided into a higher and lower town by a steep cliff which David ascended by a lift, and then took a tram to the mainly English suburb of Vittoria. At this time European colonies were still a common feature throughout South America. David was often able to mix with German, Italian or British ex-patriates, even in remote settlements far from the coast. Indeed these colonies proved to be one of the mose persuasive attractions for Mary, who was by no means certain that she would one day join David in South America. Many of these Europeans were engaged in commerce, but there were enough 'refined' people for David to be able to reassure Mary that she would still be able to play the piano, even in Brazil.

Vittoria also had a lighthouse, built in an old fort. As with several other lights which David was later to come across in South America, he sent a report back to the Stevensons in Edinburgh. This would certainly have pleased his old employers, for they strongly believed in using travel to note other people's engineering works – you never could tell when the knowledge would come in useful. This particular lighthouse seems to have held little new for David, however, for in his journal he wrote:

> 'I went up to the light-house and explained to the negro in charge that I wanted to see the light. As he did not speak English and I have no Portuguese yet, our conversation and explanations were by pantomine and you would have laughed to see us at it. The light is by reflectors and glass shades, red in front. The lamps are very old-fashioned and the whole thing very dirty. They use paraffin.'

Much of Bahia seemed to be populated by negroes, with additional English and German traders. David thought the negro waiters were the finest he had seen, but he also noted that there was still a great deal of slavery in the place. He was to discover much more evidence of slavery over the years, and it never failed to rouse the same radical political feelings he used to share with R.L.S. at Swanston, and which Mary's prim Victorian mother found so worrying.

In a hotel at Bahia David shared dinner with several local residents who seem to have delighted in telling him hair-raising stories of the Brazilian interior. The region in which he would soon be working harboured pumas and jaguars, cannibals and dangerous snakes, they said, but the 'high woods' (as the inland virgin forest was called) also swarmed with game and David regretted that he had not brought a gun, especially as he could have brought one in duty free. Youth, or high spirits, or perhaps inexperience, left him with little fear of the pumas and cannibals and his journal was much more concerned with the question of a hunting gun.

Finally David reached the port of Vittoria, where the railway survey would begin. Armed only with a kaleidoscope of first impressions of Brazil gleaned from the previous ports of call, David stepped ashore. The work he faced would not be easy, for the line was to pass first through a tropical swamp near the coast, then up through dense jungles to the high woods inland, where it would cut through hills westwards to the settlement of Natividade. On the way it would pass by several very remote townships and plantations, some of them European colonies, all struggling to make a living in the outback and desperate for a railway link to the coast. The line was needed, but to survey and build it would require courage, skill and stamina.

The proposed route was divided into sections, each with a surveyor in charge who would live with the men along the way. David was initially given a section through the coastal swamps, which was difficult work but had the compensation of being able to live in Vittoria itself, travelling out to the survey site each day until it became too distant.

As a newcomer with only a few days experience of Brazil so far, David's reaction to the future he faced now in Vittoria was often mixed, as in this early letter to Mary:

'This is by far the finest place we have been in yet as far as scenery goes, but wae's me for the hotel and the town! It is a place of about 5,000 inhabitants. The streets are lighted by gas but are in a fearful state, grass growing all over them. We are welcomed by everyone as the people who are to restore its former glory . . . We are all getting on well together. Brotherhood, the chief, has £1,200 a year, Wileman and Hamilton have £600 each and I have £400, Allanson and Culbard £250 each: so you can see I am pretty well up on the staff, and they give a very good living. It costs about £250 to £300 for each of us. I don't speak Portuguese yet but am picking it up gradually . . . We had a ride today in the woods, they are grand, all green and very thick under-growth. The cicadas kept up such a continual whistle we could hardly hear ourselves speak. We sat on a balcony smoking tonight; the weather is lovely like an English summer. The room I have here is not bad but there is a fearfully bad smell from the passage so I shall try to get it changed. There are horrible insects and such here; one of the greatest pests are the ants but I have a greater horror of beetles. They don't do so much damage but I can hear the horrible brutes moving in all directions, the woodwork is so old. I'll need to get used to them but I shan't sleep much tonight I'm afraid . . . every now and then I jump up thinking I feel one down my neck. I feel creepy as if *things* were crawling all over me. A giant cockroach or baratr has been making free with my leggings. They are not respectable like English cockroaches, nothing living here indigenous to the soil *is* respectable – dogs, pigs, even the men look disreputable. The houses are all whitewashed but they are merely white sepulchres full of noisome things!! You should see the gingerly way in which I opened my portmanteau . . . I'm laughing at myself in spite of the horrors, but I won't go to bed until the candle has burnt out, and then, oh! horrors!'

Soon David grew accustomed to the cockroaches and the other insects, however, and then the work began in the swamps. Each day David rode out to the lagoons, checking levels with a theodolite as the men, mostly locals but with a scattering of Italians, cut away the long grass and marked out with sticks where the railway line would later go. David's long descriptive letters home to Mary often paint a vivid picture of the hot, sticky day-to-day work in the swamps. Mostly they convey excitement, as if he really enjoyed the work. The hardships and dangers, though often described at length, never give the impression that he actually feared them:

'We start work at 7.00 a.m. and have our breakfasts brought out to us about 9.30. It consists of fish, omelette, beef, bread and bananas. We have limes too which we squeeze to make a first rate drink; a man carries it along with us and we drink it all day and dine at 6.00 p.m. . . . You'd hardly know me, I am growing stout and losing my

lantern jaws, but I have a good health as ever I had . . .
I am beginning to have an inkling of what people are
saying in Portuguese now but I can't keep up a general
conversation yet. Our men speak a kind of patois and
I find it very difficult to understand them or to make
myself understood. They all wear knives but the people
here are very peaceable and great cowards. We hear
dreadful accounts of up-country but I have no doubt that
much of it is exaggerated. Snakes seem to be the most
objectionable so we are taking a stock of permanganate of
potash and a syringe for injecting it. This is said to be the
best antidote . . .'

In another letter he added more of the dangers he worked
under:

'I have just come in from work and am ravenously hungry.
Hamilton and I are working together and get on very well.
We are now about 7 kilometres or 5 miles out of town, and
we have to make three traverses away from the line to get
round the swamps and over a high hill. Today we tried to
cut a picada (route) through the long grass in a swamp but
our men refused to go further than 50 yards because of the
snakes. They fired the grass to drive them out, but it would
not burn so we had to give up. We are quite accustomed to
the snakes now and really there is next to no danger with
big boots on. The snakes fly unless they have actually been
trod on . . . Along the sides of the lagoon were land crabs
in the mud; they are like sea crabs but with pretty red and
yellow rings round their bodies. They live in holes in the
bank . . .
    The Rio Doce is full of alligators, swordfish and devilfish
of enormous size; it is certain death to bathe in it.
Fortunately we do not have to cross it. No Europeans are
found on the other side, but some half-breeds, Portuguese
with Indians. The Indians are the Botacudas. We saw five
who had been kidnapped, in Vittoria the other day, and
since then they have been taken to Europe to be exhibited.
We gave them some tobacco when we saw them. The
women wear round pieces of wood in their lips and are
horrible looking as a result, and small dirty and ugly.'

The survey work was tough and long, and mostly kept David pre-occupied with day-to-day affairs, but in moments of ease, or in the evening when the men sat around by open tents or on verandahs smoking in the dusk, David would often think of home and Mary. After all, the whole reason for being in Brazil at all was to earn enough money to marry and settle down. Mary's letters from this period are tattered and almost illegible for David read and re-read them so often in his melancholic moments. Not surprisingly, perhaps, Mary felt that her news, of London and teaching and her family, must be very boring for David in the midst of his adventures, but David loved hearing of his fiancee's problems and pleasures and often reassured her in his letters that her news was not dull. Eventually, however, as the survey pushed deeper inland and he no longer lodged in Vittoria, David found the arrival of mail more erratic. Now he missed Mary even more, as in this letter:

'I sent off a letter to you this morning by our black cook Benedict, and am extremely anxiously awaiting his return as there may be an English mail in it. It is more than a fortnight since our last mail and I am wearying for letters . . .'

Sometimes the question of David's salary cropped up in letters home, for David often emphasised how much he was saving, and how cheap his living expenses were. It was almost as if he needed to reassure Mary that their separation was worthwhile and that he would eventually return home a rich man. In fact, on a salary of £400 a year plus expenses, David actually saved about £400 in the two years he spent in Brazil. As an engineer in Britain he would have earned about £100 a year, rising gradually to about £300 after some years.

David also sent lots of advice home, particularly to Mary and her family, where there was no father to take charge:

'I am glad to hear that Archie is showing good signs and hope he may not go into an office unless it is an engineer's. I still think the best thing for him is to go into some good mechanical engineering shop, and to go to the university later if he can get a scholarship or such, but after a year or two in a work-shop. It is very hard on a boy to send him into an office to waste the best years of his life when he ought to be learning something useful . . .'

In return Mary wondered anxiously whether David was attending church regularly – it evidently took her some time to realise just how remote the survey work sometimes was. David tried kindly to explain the situation:

'There are no Protestant churches in this country, but I'll go to a Catholic one when I can. We look forward to Sundays as we do no business then and do not have to rise so early. I bought an English Prayer Book and I use it, though I would rather be going with you to hear Dr. Dykes . . . Of the staff, Allanson is a Catholic, all the others are Episcopalians except myself.' And in a later letter he added:

'This is Sunday and no work; it is literally our day of rest and I spend most of it in my hammock or ship chair outside, wishing I were at home. There are no services around here, not even Roman Catholic ones nearer than the towns . . .'

Part of Mary's concern for religion may have come from David's mother. At some point after David's departure Mary visited the Angus family in Glasgow. This must have been quite a state occasion – the bright, self-confident, vigorous daughter of a manse confronting a Victorian matron with decidedly strong and oft-voiced opinions. Sadly Mary's letters of this encounter have been lost, but the meeting was evidently a great success and the Anguses took a liking to Mary. In later years she often told her daughters how Mrs. Angus first made up a cheery fire and then, pulling up her voluminous skirts (which Mary thought most inelegant and ungenteel), she settled down to a chatty conversation. 'Ah Mary', she is reported to have said, 'I was never one to gossip nor to indulge in scandal, but is it not a pleasant thing to draw one's chair up to the fire and with a friend to analeeze character,' which she then proceeded to do.

Betsy Angus was herself now a vigorous church worker in Glasgow. Mindful, perhaps, of how they had once had to struggle for a living before her husband's teaching promotion, she helped out at a soup kitchen in the Glasgow slums every Sunday before breakfast. So perhaps she seeded in Mary the concern for David's spiritual observances.

Meanwhile in Brazil, David's survey party had moved further inland. Here the forest was so dense that they could not see the sun until mid-morning, while the ground was so rough that even the mules had to be left behind as the men continued on foot. As the weather became hotter the men started to rise earlier and earlier to get as much work done as possible in the cool. It was now normal to be up by 5 a.m. as David described in one letter:

'I have been out working since six this morning and have not yet taken off my working things and there is a look about me that would get me taken up as a dangerous character in England. I was in a lovely spot under some trees for my breakfast, with mountains all around . . . the work had been very rough and I had a headache with the sun, so I sat in the shade for fully an hour and re-read all your letters since I left home and didn't I enjoy them! They are full of the subject in which I am most interested so you need not stint them. It will be about the time of your birthday when you get this, I'm sorry I can't get you anything sent. I saw some beautiful jewellery in Rio but it was too expensive and it is not safe to send anything valuable to or from here through the post. I'll bring you a birthday present when I come home.'

Christmas found David still working deep in the jungle, far from any town. The European staff made the most of their lonely situation and improvised their own celebrations, but the festivities seem to have left David more homesick than anything. He seems particularly to have recalled past winters with Mary, when they skated and held happy parties in the Drummond and Wilson houses. Like many Scots, David could slide easily from great elation into deep melancholy, as in this letter which he wrote to Mary over Christmas:

'I had felt fearfully dull all day, but meeting the others raised my spirits somewhat: we had not seen each other for a month. Hamilton and Allanson live in tents about six

miles further on, and they have invited us all there for a
Christmas dinner. This is to consist of a round of beef, a
turkey and a plum pudding. Hamilton rode the 23 miles
into the city (Vittoria) to get the materials for the pudding,
marmalade is to be used instead of peel, he has baked the
pudding himself. I will let you know how the dinner goes
off. We have been having coffee sitting outside on a big
rock and the view is quite magnificent . . .

(Later) . . . I enjoyed Christmas not so badly and was
not so miserable as I might have been. The pudding
looked quite a success outside but was rather doughy
inside. We had some music – bagpipes – and the Italian
workmen outside sang very well too, but then a storm
began, the biggest thunder-storm I have ever seen, I've
never seen such lightning. It lasted two hours and then got
quiet. We got very little wet inside the tents. It began
about 7.30 p.m. just after we had finished dinner. About
9.30 p.m. our mules were caught and we started back. It
was pitch dark and raining heavily but we enjoyed our ride
immensely, our mules slipping about on the wet roads
which here and there are flooded. At one flooded stream
my mule refused, and he and I quarrelled. I spurred him
and he reared up and we both fell over and rolled in the
stream. My foot was caught in the stirrup and it was lively
for a minute or two, but I managed to break the spur and
got loose and soon got hold of the burroo and pulled him
out . . . You and Jessie will be home just now and having a
good time I hope, with plenty of frosty weather and skating
and other nice things. I am glad you are anxious for my
letters, it shows you have not forgotten me yet.'

Mary, who was still a teacher in London, returned home for
her Christmas holiday and for a while all the old friends, except
David, were reunited. David's bright personality was certainly
missed, but there was a compensation – he had sent a crate of
pineapples from Brazil. These were such a rare treat in
Edinburgh that he was hailed by all as a great 'public
benefactor' and so contrived to be the star of the show even in
his absence.

By the New Year David had become indifferent to the
dangers of working in swamp and jungle. Unpleasant stinging

creatures, the steamy climate, lack of regular food supplies, impassable roads and the many other problems which he and his workmen faced (and which mostly he had to solve) were described almost casually in letters. He really had little concern for dangers, as in this letter from January 1883:

'I rode home from Culbard's house through a thunderstorm and fearful rain, it was about as unpleasant an experience as anyone could wish for . . . my wretched mule shied every minute and I could feel him trembling under me so I walked him for about half-way, mostly through water. I had a bath as soon as I arrived and then dinner and took my quinine before dinner – horrible, but duty is duty you know. I'm doctor for this section and have doctored three men who had intermittent fever and they are getting on alright. Yesterday I had a fearful day's work about four miles through deep swamp . . . One of the men was bitten by a water snake, but none of the water snakes are deadly which is a comfort. I was stung tonight by a *mourrumboundas,* quite badly stung and I'm all swelled up and sore . . . Our dinner tonight was good – soup made from Liebeg's Extract, some Paysandu tongue left over from yesterday, fish bought last night for a milreis, galena (chicken) bought a week ago and fed in the kitchen on mealies; it loses in muscle and gains in flesh. We have run out of bread and have to eat arroz (rice) and fiejas (black beans) and farniha with these delicacies. There is also fruit and then coffee and a smoke.

 . . . We move to Pitanga on Tuesday or Wednesday and I have made arrangements to take our baggage by bullock cart, the only wheeled vehicle in the province, and it is an institution. These carts consist of two solid wooden wheels fixed to an axle piece and a bottom of flat boards for the carrying part. They are drawn by six oxen in pairs and the wheels make a fearful screeching and groaning as they move, they sound not unlike the bag-pipes in the distance . . . Our work is gettng on very satisfactorily and Brotherhood (David's chief) gave me some encouragement this week. He told me that if everyone worked as I did we would finish in no time. I've got a bad section of the swamp but I get on famously with my men. However all the older men on the job tell me I'll drop this style of working when I have been longer in Brazil. I don't feel any inclination to do so yet and I'll try to keep it up.'

The vigorous style was, of course, typical of David's nature, but he had yet to learn to pace himself properly in the energy-sapping climate of the interior. Eventually exhaustion did overtake him, and for three weeks he was stranded miles from any other European, sick with bouts of recurrent fever. This first experience of a tropical illness seems to have been quite difficult, even for a robust and powerful man like David, but typically it was only mentioned here and there in letters home:

'I was never so tired before, nearly asleep and sore all over with riding. The other day a man handed me a sprig of something to smell at dinner, it is rather like the wild thyme at home. He told me it was called Santa Maria – and I thought of Scotland and *my own* Santa Maria, a minha santa. I was quite alone last night in our old house, no-one within a mile of me, but it was moonlight and very beautiful. Don't stint your letters thinking I may tire of them, they are my principal literature here and every trivial incident is of interest . . . Good-night, I'm sorry I'm not there to say it in person.'

A few days later he wrote:

'. . . Your letters were sent to Wileman by mistake and I only received them on Thursday – they were such good ones they cured me – I did not find any kindly disposed female to nurse me, the only nurse I had was my black cook Benedict and he was a good one . . . Nobody came near me when I was at my worst. The chief and most of the men were up at the Rio Doce early on the morning I took ill, and were away for a fortnight. Luckily one of the men came back here for orders as to some of the things he was taking up and I kept him with me and got him to give me water and look after me generally. I am in much better spirits today and got some work done. One of the worst things for me while I was ill was that I knew my section was at a standstill, and if I had been ill longer they might have sent me home. I'm afraid you will think this a terribly dismal letter, but I'm not dismal, I'm just anxious about my work, as the better I do here the sooner I'll be able to come home and claim you . . . You must excuse my writing, my hand shakes so. I was never so weak as I was this month – but I think it was good for me, as I thought that I was going to carry all before me here and now I know that I am not. I was in hopes they would raise my salary to £600 but now my work is not so far forward as it was. It needs a man to come to a place like this and be ill to know the value of home. I've lain and thought how I'd give anything to be back home again to see anyone who would look after me. I hate this place . . . I will stay till I finish unless I get very unwell and get sent home, but I'm not coming back here again.'

Entries in David's diary illustrate better how he worried about his work as he lay ill:

January 23rd: 'Very ill today . . . about as miserable as I well can be and able to do no work . . . Had ague today.'
January 24th: 'Still very ill. Managed to get plan laid out on table and did some work . . .'
January 25th: 'Still ill but not so weak – ague today – I got some work on plan . . .'

Eventually David recovered and returned to work. By now the sections allotted to the various engineers were being completed and meetings were sometimes held to detail how the different parts were to link up. One of these was held at a place called Santa Theresa, where Wileman (the second in command of the survey) lived. He had a prefabricated iron house which he evidently re-erected whenever he moved on to another section. David found the garden filled with English roses and lettuces, and there was even talk of planting strawberries. This must have had quite an influence on young David, because from then on he always seemed to bring a touch of home to his own out-back houses. Years later, for example, time would find him living in a typical Paraguayan hacienda – but with a very English tennis court! Meanwhile he settled for reading old copies of the *Scotsman* newspaper sent out to him from home.

His own camp was certainly very different from Wileman's house:

'I wish you could see me, I've arranged my sleeping place so that I get none of the rain that comes in here and there. I'm sitting on a stool by a table, my bed is in front and my hammock is behind me. All around me are boxes of provisions and working materials and my drawing table. I've bought a dog to guard the house and tents. There are very few dangers here except bad health: my men are all faithful especially Benedict who is a black jewel. In future I intend to get up about 3.30 a.m., then I can stop at 10.00 a.m. and do some paper work in the hut and so avoid working in the heat of the sun. It is Sunday today and I have just read a service to myself and a lesson from your Testament. It seems queer to be reading the service alone so far from other Englishmen . . .'

At about the same time, in February 1883, Mary's mother and her brother Tom both became sick. Mrs. Wilson had abcesses in her ear and a high fever – problems which can be easily dealt with today but which could be serious just a century ago. The Ryans and others rallied round to look after the Wilsons while in London Mary waited, and dreaded, the annual school inspection. Her mother's illness could not have come at a worse time, for next year's grant from the Board of Education depended on the performance of her pupils during the inspection. But then her sister Georgie also fell ill and Mrs. Drummond called for Mary and Jessie to leave London and return to Edinburgh as family nurses. From then on Mary lived in Edinburgh, looking after her mother, keeping house and mothering the four younger children still at school. She never went back to her London teaching.

By July the aurist and a doctor were still attending Mrs. Wilson. Sometimes she had to be lanced behind one ear, but Mary was always there to look after her mother. By now Georgie was well and had gone off to Lausanne as an au paire, but the younger children still needed looking after. The Scottish Education Department would not accept Mary's London teaching qualifications so in Edinburgh she could only find occasional part-time teaching in private schools. This was undoubtedly a tough time for the Wilsons – in one letter Mary wrote:

> 'The beginning of the week is now a blank to me as I did nothing but sit and sew dresses ready to come away: I had simply got into a state of rags. One is such a pretty new dress. I should like to be photographed in it, and if I am it will be for you . . .'

By now David had paid off the debt to his father, who had lent £200 for tropical clothing and surveying instruments. He now began to send money home, some to be saved for the future but some to help the Wilsons through this difficult period. In fact David's finances were by now really quite sound. In July he sent money to his sister Isabella for the purchase of an engagement ring for Mary (he had been too poor to buy one before his departure for Brazil), and along with this he also sent enough for Isabella to buy a brooch for his aunt, his mother and for Mrs. Wilson. At about this time he also heard from his brother James, who was now an up-and-coming success in San Francisco. He urged David to invest some of his earnings, and later David sent James some diamonds bought in Rio but which would sell for a profit in America.

By autumn David had spent his first year in South America, learning of the hardships and pleasures of surveying in remote country. He undoubtedly got on well with his men – not surprising really, for this was a hallmark of his teachers the Stevensons, but just as importantly, he faced the question of relating to the other Europeans. David was undoubtedly the hale-and-hearty type, a lively, gregarious, even conceited young man, but how would this go down with a mixed band of men thrown together by a distant parent company in London? In one letter David described his colleagues as they sat around him one evening:

> 'There are four of us here, Culbard, 30 years of age, brownish red hair, 6 foot 1 inch, Scotch, strongly argumentative and pig-headed. Allanson, about 45 to 50 years of age, 5 foot 4 inches tall, indifferent colouring, a decent old man, fearfully innocent and an R.C. He is married and has a large family, one of whom is in Rome

coming out to be a priest. Victor Hugo, a Pole, fair moustache, good looking, 5 foot 10 inches tall, slightly lame, speaks broken English but not a bad fellow, but he takes Culbard's part in arguments and is also pig-headed when backed by Culbard, amenable on his own. Angus, aged 27, I needn't describe him as I think you've seen him and might not recognise the portrait I would paint. We get along very well together. I'm boss, I'm also the youngest, the benjamin in fact.'

These men were David's equals in Brazil, but even his superiors were not beyond comment: 'I was delighted to hear the Scots had done so well at Wimbledon and intend to rub it into Brotherhood when I see him. He's anti-Scotch, at any rate he is ultra-English and a fierce conservative. I can make him get into a beautiful passion by launching out into politics and finishing up on Scotland and England!'

This cocky self-confidence was a characteristic which Mary disapproved of in her fiancee, and for the rest of her life she tried to make him change, without much success. Even now she seems to have mentioned it in letters, for David replied:

'Perhaps it is as well you did not send Arthur Doyle's opinion of me, for you can see my conceit has not decreased though I give it another name – but no matter . . .'

Sometimes the descriptions of his colleagues were more picturesque than conceited though, for in truth David enjoyed their familiar company just as he had once enjoyed the Edinburgh set:

'It has been hotter than ever today. After breakfast we sat out on the verandah and had half an hour's smoke – it would have made a good picture, Culbard and I all in white with big straw hats, Victor Hugo in yellow top boots, pink coat and light breeches. He had on a wide-awake hat and sat on the door sill. It was broiling and though we were in the shade the whole air felt as if we were in an oven. We will have a smoke by star-light after dinner. I can see the moons of Jupiter with the binoculars your mama gave me . . .'

Meanwhile the work continued, pushing deeper into the interior. David's letters described his progress on one section:

'One hill we climbed and sat on a rock at the top and smoked. We went to see the general lie of the country and it was a grand view. All along the way we were among thickly wooded hills and valleys, not big enough for mountains. Itapicu is a mountain about 18 miles from here and is shaped like a needle or a pillar. I am to carry a picada (route) along the sides of the mountains from Ramillettie's House to Itapicu, when I have finished laying down my old section . . .'

Later: 'I expect to finish all the plans and papers on my first section in about a fortnight and then Victor Hugo and I go up to Ramillettie's House and survey down along the sides of the mountains to Itapicu. It is virgin forest so I hope it won't be as hot as here: this is the hottest and unhealthiest month but it is also the end of the hot season . . .'

Later still: 'We rode over to Itapicu this morning and saw Capitas Necco's widow on the way – he was assassinated by one of his slaves two years ago in Cachoeria. Then we rode down by the foot of the mountain we have to traverse along and found a beautiful little green valley near a water-mill where we decided to pitch our tents when we start work. It is quite near our work but we will have to cut a road up the mountain through the high woods to where our line will run . . . Before we got to Itapicu we had something of an adventure. We came to a stream in heavy flood, rushing down at a great rate with water about 8 feet deep. We held a council of war as we did not want to get our clothes wet. We decided to strip and ride or rather swim our mules across, we on them, holding our clothes well above our heads. Once we were stripped our mules did not recognise us and were in a great state of fright. We had a good laugh thinking what we would do if they broke away and fled while we were in a state of nudity! However we managed to swim them across without wetting our clothes, then dressed on the other side and continued our journey.'

This section was evidently tough work, and in another letter David described how frustrating it could sometimes be:

'This is the place for bad temper – it's awful what furies I've been in with my men and what language I've used. But when you have at last planted a marker pole one mile away, over the roughest ground imaginable, to cross which takes two hours at least, and that pole *must* remain in sight in order to get your line continued, and then one of the men (sent back to get something else) thinks to himself, "I'll save time and another journey by collecting that pole now", *then* is the time to see a man stamp on his hat if it's a soft one, and generally make himself disagreeable and lively!'

As the work progressed towards Itapicu, David and his workers had to keep moving camp. Generally they tried to rent a house from the local people, and for a few weeks tents and store houses would spring up round about, before disappearing again as the men moved on. Since most people were wretchedly poor, David rarely found a good house in which to work and sleep – indeed he sometimes had to share with the owners and even their animals:

'We stayed the night at the Fazenda Moreno in a room 10 feet by 6 feet. I was in a camp-bed and Victor was in a hammock and it *was* cold. Below our room the pigs seemed to lodge and they had an unsavoury odour and grunted considerably. The floor was of loose boarding and of great age and holely, very holely: it required care and agility to keep from joining our neighbours below . . . We are much bothered with vampire bats – none of them has attacked any of us yet – there is one in the room now about 10 inches or more over the wings.'

There was a joy, an unpredictability, about surveying which David found very satisfying. Quite often the men worked in completely untouched forest where only local Indians lived. Indeed the nearby Rio Doce river marked the edge of head-hunter cannibal territory, the graveyard of numerous exploration parties and Jesuit missionaries. This was excitement of a kind the construction men would never enjoy, for they would be following the route already prepared by the surveyors.

There were hazards everywhere in loneliness – Victor Hugo had once lain with a twisted knee for over a month on a mountain side, accompanied by six faithful Indians and living only on roots and leaves, until he was found by a search party expecting only to bury him. There were unexpected moments of emotion too: David once sheltered from a cloud-burst in the hovel of a slave called Marguerita. Here he huddled with a pack of half-starved dogs and a large flock of ducks as the rain formed a pool of water several inches deep all over the floor. On occasions like this an enormous sympathy for Brazil's poor always seemed to well up in David, to come pouring out in some future letter home. There was also the man whom David befriended as his men plotted their survey along a mountain side. From then on two baskets of oranges were sent to David and his men up the hillside every day as a gift.

Dangers from animals were a more common problem, but these never seemed to frighten David. He always seemed to see the comical side of the dogs tearing out of the undergrowth, yelping hysterically with a mountain lion in hot pursuit, even of the cobra snakes, which he here combines with an amusing description of a winged grasshopper: 'I killed a large cobra surucucu in the picada the other morning. It is one of the worst snakes we have here, with a poison fang in its head and a poison spur in its tail. The baratras muster in force still and a new bechu has appeared, of a bright green colour. He doesn't hurt but as he is large and apparently rather short-sighted he causes some excitement when he comes violently in contact with the head or any other exposed part.'

In another letter he was just as off-hand about the rats in his digs: 'I also got a new house for my men higher up the hill, but in 20 minutes they were back carrying a cobra-coral on a stick. They informed me that they would rather walk up from their old house in the mornings as this one was already tenanted – literally swarming with snakes! We have nothing in this house worse than rats, but their number is enormous and they are quite tame and impudent. I don't mind when they behave reasonably but it is carrying matters to extreme when they have a pitched battle in the beams overhead during the night and wake you up with their screaming and then they drop – thud, thud, thud – to the floor and sometimes into your bed . . .'

David also had a sharp eye for local detail, which he often described to Mary in that unique humourous way of his – the washerwomen who beat the clothes on large stones: 'It is rather hard on the clothes but it keeps the haberdashers from starving.' Or the tarantula spider which Benedict caught: 'We put a penholder between his fangs and he nearly bit it through. A saucer would not cover him, and as he was too big to dry I have put him in a bottle of spirit.' Then there was a collection of slave huts which reminded him of Uncle Tom's Cabin: 'They are in a miserable state, in rags and nearly starving, but their masters are little better off, for although a man may have a large extent of land and slaves he may have no food and no money: the railway will change all this, as then they will be able to get their coffee, sugar and so on to the seaports to sell it there, and then the land will increase in value too.' Some of the slaves also had dogs: 'We are great favourites in this district, but our greatest admirers are the dogs, who all put on a look of contentment whenever we appear. Every man, even the slaves, keeps several dogs and the consequence is that all the dogs are a walking personification of famine. When they discovered that we would not ill-treat them, they came to us in shoals. Several come a distance of miles at meal times, and start home immediately afterwards, and to see us at meals you would think we kept a big kennel, whereas only seven or eight belong to us.'

Eventually David completed the section to Itapicu and he was now sent on to a section which ran along the banks of the Rio Doce river. This meant a welcome return to Vittoria for 'a glimpse of civilisation and "b'iled shirts" which are unknown as far inland as this', before heading up the river by canoe. The first base was about eighty miles upriver, and here David had the men erect a house or ranch. It stood on legs, with creepers interlaced to form the sides and coca leaves matted to make an almost-watertight roof. This was David's office, where he slept in a hammock, made his careful survey calculations and drawings, and got to know the various hazardous creatures of the river: 'During the day an insect – known to the natives by the name "Borrachudos" – musters in millions. When one gets under your skin it looks a dot but it rapidly grows to a fair size on your blood, when it flies away again. My hands were fearfully swelled the first two days but I rubbed them with spirit of camphor and they are getting better . . . There is a great deal of game around here, oncas (pumas), tapirs, peccaries and monkeys . . . Alligators float around in the river, even sharks come up as far as this . . . This is a beautiful place, high woods for seventy miles below, with here and there a tiny clearing, like ours here, looking as if it were going to be crushed by the encircling woods.'

David soon made friends with a young monkey which liked to sit on his feet as he wrote letters home, but his favourite pet was a pig which lived a precarious life between David and the bacon slicer. 'It leads a rather uncomfortable existence on account of the dogs who get up a pig-hunt whenever it puts in an appearance. It is the rummest beast and follows me about all day like a dog. The first day the men caught it they painted it all over a bright red colour. I hope it won't hurt him, but it makes him easily distinguished and less likely to get shot (the men had to hunt for their food each day). The dogs now fear and respect him for he is master and makes any number of dogs under nine or ten turn tail. Sometimes they go for him by the dozen, and they all tear round and round the ranch, and we are kept running from the door in front to the door at the back to see which dog is nearest to him when he turns. Our principal objection to this pig is that he and the dogs sometimes get up an argument in the night and forget that they are not alone: then in the morning there is a great searching for slippers, candlesticks and such-like which have been thrown at them.'

Eventually the work was completed. Each day David moved further upstream and then surveyed back again to a camp which had meanwhile been cut out of the river bank. This involved clearing the undergrowth, cutting ditches to the river, laying sand for a tent base, unpacking the lamps, trestles and hammocks, erecting an open-air kitchen and then going off into the woods to shoot supper. Quite often it was dark before David returned, canoeing by moonlight down-stream towards the camp fire. Sometimes David and a few men would march off into the hills looking for short-cuts for the railway where the river made a long loop.

David described some of his work in his diary:

August 28th: 'I went out with theodolite and traversed towards Santa Suzanne – got to within 1½ kilometres. Ground rough. Petros chaining, Liupe taking cross sections. Squad cutting cross sections and Aureliano cutting main picada . . .'

September 11th: 'Weighed out provisions etc. for the workmen who go with Aureliano. Got away about 6.30 and arrived at Sta. S. about 9. We had breakfast on the sand, the cookboy making a fire and heating up the feijao we had brought . . .'

Then one day the survey leader Brotherhood arrived with the news that the second-in-command Wileman had been sacked. 'Wileman has been at work with a staff three times as strong as any other since Christmas, on a section at least a quarter less in size than this one and no more difficult than my last section, yet his plans are not in, and by all accounts he is not able to get a line complying with the Government's conditions, and now I am to go and do it for him. My expenses on the last section were about £540 in all, yet as salary out of that I only drew £100 . . . Wileman's section has cost not less than £2,200, his salary for the period being £450. Even now it is doubtful if his work is any use and he has been nine months in finding out his errors and all that money has been spent uselessly . . .'

Brotherhood obviously admired David's engineering and administrative abilities, and now as the survey neared completion the question of who might be kept on for the construction of the railway line arose. David faced a dilemma, knowing that he stood a good chance of further work and yet desperately anxious to see Mary again. His solution was that Mary should come to Brazil, where they would marry and face the adventure of out-back life together:

'When you write don't say "*do what you think best*", but say definitely if you will be willing to come out to me if I can't get home . . . If you won't come out, then I won't stay: that is why I want to know what you have to say about it, so that I may be able to give an answer to the firm if I am asked to stay. I won't decide until I hear from you. I expect the offer will be at least £600 a year with servants and a house found. Now we couldn't get anything like that in England – probably not even as much as we could save here. Here I have a fine record so far and expect to get on well, while in England there are thousands of engineers . . .'

It is clear, however, that Mary and her family were hoping that David would come home and find work in Britain. Mary's mother, worried perhaps at the idea of losing her daughter-nurse, urged her not to rush into marriage with a young man whose prospects were very uncertain and whom she had not even seen for eighteen months. The family doctor said that Mary's own health might not stand up to the rigours of South America, while Mary was reluctant to leave her mother, who was still unwell (her ears were now being lanced by the celebrated Dr. Joseph Bell himself). Friends argued that even David's descriptions of Brazil were hardly inviting to a young lady: 'Craufurd and Morrow have been much bothered with *jiggers,* a bechu that goes under the skin and turns into a bag of eggs making a bad and ugly sore. They have to be cut out . . .'

In addition, Mrs. Wilson was a Tory, and still worried about David's radical politics. He, admittedly, was not very careful to hide them from her, complaining openly that the students of Edinburgh University had elected a Tory rector, and writing 'I ain't going to answer your Tory pleadings, it's the usual stuff. Every man ain't born to a certain station in life, and if all men were or had been contented to remain in this said state, the world would have stayed still and we'd be Picts yet. I have no fear of Scotland's ever being such a miserable country as Ireland. Scotland has always been more Liberal and willing to advance . . .'

If anything, the poverty and squalor of Brazil reinforced this radical view, for by now David had experiences far beyond the understanding of Mrs. Wilson in Edinburgh. In particular slavery, supposedly abolished in 1871, still existed in Brazil:

'You needn't mind my politics. I'm for what's right whether it is Liberal or Conservative, give every man his due. It gives a good hard knock to an Englishman's ideas of right and wrong and "legal rights" when he sees a country like this and finds a man who is well educated (for a Brazilian) and kind-hearted enough – kicking or going for old slaves because they're too old to walk the 20 miles from one Fazenda to another when the family flits without breaking down on the road. I saw a Fazendeiro flitting some days ago; in the forenoon the family passed in a machine drawn by mules, and in the evening about 20 or 30 slaves passed, two or three very old ones last, and one old woman, lame and twisted by rheumatism or something, took fully 30 minutes to walk out of sight – about seventy yards. I never saw such a sight. I never had much sympathy for folks who are murdered in slave risings and I've less now. Better heaps of murders if it stops the misery these wretches have to endure. When a slave passes a free man he holds out his hand and asks a blessing. That old woman had to walk a further ten miles and I'm wondering what she thought about on the way. I'd like to know to what she looks forward to, they have no religion to speak of.'

Finally Mary's brother Tom said that she should not go to Brazil and that seemed to close the matter, though it left David angry and bitter: 'I didn't expect Tom's consent for you to come out to Brazil or anywhere else. He's not thinking of you, but what he would miss if you were away. Why, he could hardly exist if it weren't for someone looking after him . . .' Nevertheless, poor David now realised that Mary would not be coming out to marry him in Brazil. What was he now to do?

At about this time news began to filter in that the railway would not be built immediately. The money had not yet been raised and all the men were to be paid off. Most of the other engineers seemed to have plans and schemes to follow up in South America and there must have been a lot of table talk of the wealth of opportunities which still existed, despite the disappointing railway news.

For a time David was asked to design a new harbour at Vittoria. 'I drew out a design of concrete blocks and sent it to Hunt, who asked me if we could build it *in situ*. I told him I thought it could, though this had never been done yet in such deep water, but that I'd rather do it so. He agreed, remarking "Write a paper on the construction for the Institute of Civil Engineers when it is completed".'

David had so much hoped to return home to his fiancee, but this scheme kept him long enough in Brazil to be lured by the prospect of more work. 'I'm kind of afraid of being out of work,' he wrote to Mary, 'I've never been yet and it's an experience I don't exactly pant after . . .' Then he was offered an introduction to influential people in Buenos Aires in the Argentine and sadly he took the chance. He sent another £80 back to Mary to add to their savings, and a box of insects and reptiles in bottles to Tom. Then he took a ship for Buenos Aires.

Chapter Four

MARRIED AT LAST 1884-1886

In March 1884 Brotherhood, leader of the Brazilian survey, gave David a 'smashing testimonial'. With this, and a few letters of introduction (for the engineering fraternity in South America seems to have operated through a web of personal contact and recommendation), David travelled to Buenos Aires. Soon he found work with the British firm of Prebble and Ware as an engineer in charge of constructing a section of the railway then being built along the River Parana from Buenos Aires to the inland city of Rosario. David's section was well up-stream, beginning at Campana but centred on the small town of San Nicolas, and stretching for about 100 kilometres towards Rosario. David's friend Bernard Culbard, another surveyor from Brazil, was given a section of the same railway and they were able to visit each other quite often.

By April winter was beginning to arrive. David soon found the chilly weather and the endless flat grazing lands with their herds of cattle, sheep and horses very different from the high woods and warmer climate of Brazil. However there were compensations, for quite a few Europeans lived in Buenos Aires and Rosario. David even found a 'Scotch Church' in Buenos Aires: 'The congregation was not large, but I liked the service and thought I was home again. I think of taking a sitting (i.e. renting a regular seat in church). Even though I shall be up country I'd like to have a connection with the church,' he wrote, tactfully mindful of his mother's and Mrs. Wilson's concern for his church attendance.

David also discovered a frozen meat factory at Campana, run by a John Angus (although he was not related). At that time refrigeration was still a novelty, and the idea that meat could be shipped across the world and still reach Britain in a fresh state was quite remarkable. 'We went through the meat freezing place at Campana and saw their processes,' wrote David. 'They simply compress air and then suddenly expand it, this produces intense cold of about 30 degree Fahr. and the sheep are frozen hard as wood. The air becomes like snow. On board the steamers they have the same engines for compressing air and that keeps the meat frozen: 15,000 carcasses are going home by the steamer sailing now . . . ' Then as if the two were connected, he went on: 'Meat is very cheap, living is not expensive, the hotel is cheaper than in England too and will only cost me about £12 a month . . . If I stay with these people it will be two years before I can get home. If you would rather come out and be married here *I will be only too glad*: but I'm willing to do whatever you think fit.' David still hoped feebly that Mary and her mother would relent, and later letters continued to stress the attractions of life in Argentina – but to no avail.

In Buenos Aires there was an English circus, and even a skating rink where David could renew old pleasures and think of Mary and Edinburgh. He also visited an old acquaintance: 'I called on Connacher today at the Scottish School. He was once head-master of Cauvin's Institution in Duddingston, where I had part of my education. I found him teaching about a dozen boys Euclid. There seems to be a great number of children in the school and not bad looking either . . . Buenos Aires is not nearly so fine a city as Rio but it has its advantages and there seems to be much more energy and work about . . . '

In June David finally moved upriver to his quarters at San Nicolas. It was an unpromising, wintry start, as David wrote: 'I came up from Campana by steamer but I didn't enjoy the passage. About 5.00 a.m. on a mighty cold and dark morning they put me ashore on a pontoon moored in front of the town, and the last thing I noticed as the steamer left was one of my iron boxes still lying on it, and not labelled.'

As resident engineer in charge, David was supposed to have a house for office use, but the wooden building with corrugated iron roof intended for him was still being built. As a result he moved into a hotel, but when he found he had to ride several miles out to camp each day to supervise the work he soon gave this up and moved into a tent on site. Here he was blue with cold most of the time, but at least it was close to the work, and the missing iron box even turned up after a few days. Nevertheless, with every day the weather became colder as winter set in: 'When we rise in the morning we find the ground white with hoar frost which lies for some hours and all the water around here is frozen. I believe we may have skating yet! The middle of winter is not come either – June 21st is our shortest day . . . '

Although the men were already preparing the ground for railway lines when David first arrived, his most important task was to construct first a long jetty at San Nicolas to allow steamers to unload construction materials. For a time the area was a hive of industry and the jetty crept out into the river as David launched into the work with customary enthusiasm. But then problems arose:

'I am in charge of this section, but although they want the work pressed forward, I have been written to or telegraphed every day during the fortnight I have been here, with different orders. It seems they could not get settled with the proprietors of the land, and when that was done they still had to settle about the pier. They ordered me to stop work, which I did for an hour or two, but later put the men on again and worked away. Then the Captain of the Port of San Nicolas sent me down word he'd stop me if we began building the pier again, and they telegraphed from B.A. not to quarrel with him . . . '

In fact David ignored the threat and carried on, determined to create a good impression by being well on with his work when he next went to Buenos Aires. Soon after he was indeed summoned to a meeting, having meanwhile heard nothing more from the Captain of the Port. As he waited outside the office, some of the other young engineers also waiting there sympathised with him on his delay. 'I let them rip till they had pitied me enough. Then I told Clarke that I'd have the rails laid the day after they reached me, even if they came this week, and that we'd be out to the pier head by the weekend and ready to discharge ocean liners the next week!' David thought it great fun to put his rivals back in their places. In the event the company representative said he would have ignored the order to stop, and David for once kept tactfully silent.

As soon as David was back on site the work continued, to the apparent concern of a large crane which fished each day close by and 'looks across at us working, and seems to think we have no right here. If he knew how to go about it legally I'm sure he would take out an interdict against us.' David's energies clearly met with company approval, however, for a friend reported over-hearing a discussion 'by some of the big-wigs and that I was considered the best of the lot . . .' as a result of which David was put in charge of all workings in his section and given an immediate credit facility of £1,000 at a bank in Buenos Aires.

Before long problems reappeared, and it says much for David's personality and energies that his work was not seriously delayed. 'I am almost in despair for want of carpenters without whom I might almost as well not be here,' he wrote in July. 'Then the Captain of the Port has had no official papers and is still afraid to let me go on lest he gets into trouble: to crown all the Customs authorities sent word that they intend to measure the ground we are on and charge us for the use of it, so I'm properly mewed up on every side.'

Later he wrote: 'For six weeks now I have had to do everything, be office boy, tracer, engineer, draughtsman, time-keeper, store-keeper and general foreman of all the work! A man with such multifarious employ has not much time on his hands, especially when he had no better-half to console and flatter him (but we'll cure that in a little I hope).'

Finally in mid-July David persuaded the skipper of the steamer *Handel* to discharge his cargo at the newly-completed jetty. The operation went smoothly, much to David's relief, for another 30,000 tons of construction material was due to arrive on more steamers as work on the railway itself resumed. Soon local people were actually coming to watch the ocean-going vessels unloading 'in a stream which they have thought of for years as not much more than a ditch' he wrote with satisfaction. Then a railway was laid from the harbour to the worksite, although manhandling the heavy cargoes from the ships onto the pier remained a difficulty.

Meanwhile David was given a carriage by the company to let him commute between his house (now completed) and the jetty. Quite often he had also to pick up visiting officials and dignitaries and take them on conducted tours round his works, which explains why he had a carriage and not just a horse; it also gave his position an air of some authority in letters home – though Mary remained unconvinced.

Work on laying the actual rails went slowly, mainly because the marker poles on the route had been staked out carelessly before David's arrival. 'In the office they complain greatly of it, and it was even said to Morrow and I who were there at the time "it's a pity you two didn't come down six weeks sooner and go in on the staking out of the line".' David would probably have enjoyed that, for as he wrote in another letter, 'I don't like construction as well as exploration, it's too slow.'

Perhaps David was also thinking of the problems which could crop up to frustrate a constructor. His letters were scattered with endless examples: 'For some days my life has been a burden on account of having to pay the men: it is much harder to me than any other work I have done, and has taken up my time to the expense of other work. The reason is this: there are several different currencies, and each man has his own, and goes into lengthy and deep calculations to find out what he has been paid in terms of his own currency.'

On another day he wrote: 'You have no idea of the troubles that beset me in this frightful country: everyone delays in every possible way and the Government is the worst offender of all. The national proverb – manana – by which the whole population stands is – never do today what can possibly be put off till tomorrow.'

Later he noted: 'I am in a great peck of troubles just now about the rail-laying, which I have to push at both ends and which is constantly being stopped by the bridges ... The greatest difficulty we have is the getting of bricks and sand, and I have to do a lot of trotting about looking after these.'

Quite a few small rivers flowed into the River Parana, each requiring to be bridged as the railway snaked forward towards Rosario. David constructed at least six major bridges on his section on line. One of the most important was a large bridge near San Nicolas over a small river called the Arroyo Ramallo. First David had to find a suitable site, and then, as he described in a letter to Mary: 'We had to find the owners and make a bargain with then – sucking maté while the bargain was in the making. Sucking maté (South American tea) is a religious ceremony here: a small nut or shell three inches long by two inches in diameter is filled with maté. Into this small jug is put a long tube of metal, silver or brass, with a nozzle at the end. This tube gets about red hot in a minute or two, and when the host hands it to a stranger he usually burns himself the first time he tries it, takes the skin off his lips, trying to suck. The maté pot goes all round the crowd, the same pot and the same tube, and continues to go round for hours in fact it may go round for days! A small boy usually goes round with the pot and keeps the maté boiling. Well, we drank, or rather sucked, the said maté for an hour and a half with a dozen or so half starved hounds snarling around, and at last we got a bargain made with the owners of the ground. Then I had four days riding over the line from the beginning of my section measuring up the earthworks.'

Soon the construction work began, done mostly by a gang of Italian navvies under David's watchful eye. 'Today and yesterday I had to set out the columns for the Arroyo Ramallo bridge,' he wrote. 'It was very particular work and I had to be very careful with it.' Then in a letter to Mary he added 'It is the highest bridge in the province and will be very good looking when it is finished.' David always found great satisfaction in a completed job well done; engineering did at least offer the pleasure of something to see for his efforts which surveying did not. At the end of February 1885 the bridge was completed.

Meanwhile other bridges were also under construction – one at the Arroyo les Hermanos, and another with three spans of 130 feet at the Arroyo del Medio. For a time winter held up the work as frost hardened the ground and cold winds whistled across the flat plains, but by August construction had resumed and the various bridges were well advanced.

Progress on the railway itself also improved as winter retreated and the ground thawed out, enabling workmen to lay sleepers and hammer in the iron spikes which held each rail in place. By now a stream of vessels was unloading materials onto the jetty at San Nicolas, and work soon began on constructing a number of beautiful little country stations along the line. David took as much pride in these small wayside halts as any architect would have done for a palace. The ships, however, prompted David's mother to remind him of the evils of smuggling – this has caused family mirth ever since, for she evidently imaged her son might be imitating the activities of his grandfather years earlier on the River Tay. As the respectable wife of a schoolmaster, she was anxious to live down this aspect of the family's history, but to David it must also have shown how little the folks back home understood the life he led in South America, despite his long and vivid letters.

One of the attractions of David's work was the variety of each day. It may have been a frustrating life fraught with responsibility, tight deadlines and unforeseen difficulties (for example the local currency had just been devalued and the men now wanted payment in gold), but at least life was never grey or predictable. David Angus never had to endure the fixed hours or humdrum life of a Victorian shop or factory manager, far less that of an office or factory worker. So long as the work progressed, he could usually set his own hours, eat when he decided, and relax when he needed to. The colour of life also varied as he moved from one work site to another, or from city to open country – he never had to face a lifetime of journeys through the same streets to work each day. There was a freedom to his work which millions of Victorians at home hardly knew even existed – and he loved it.

One good example of the colourful side of South American life was the annual Carnival, once a religious festival but an event which had been adapted, even in David's time, into something more like a party, and which the entire south American population celebrates even today. David's descriptions of Carnival were, of course, those of the more genteel, usually foreign, population in the small town of San Nicolas. But even here the Italians, Irish and English residents had their own fun, while the local workers drank and danced elsewhere.

'Carnival began last Sunday and continued Monday and Tuesday,' wrote David to Mary. 'Today it is to be buried. Carnival largely consists in throwing water or such! from a bucket, jug or other article or squirting it from a kind of syringe, called a *pomo*, on any party of the opposite sex who happens to be around, and this intellectual amusement is called *playing pomo*. The club in San Nicolas gave a masked ball in the evening and sent us all invitations. We all went, the ladies are masked and wear dominoes and ask the gentlemen to dance. The ball began at 1.00 a.m. and we left at 4.00 a.m. so I don't know what time it broke up, but I didn't care for it . . . I have been dreaming for the last two nights that I was home and we were married – you are my only want.'

Christmas 1884 came, and with it two cards from Mary. In South America it was summer and trees were in fruit – David was even suffering from prickly heat. More than a dozen vessels were unloading at the pier, where rails were now stacked 15 feet high. There had just been a flood, David was missing Buenos Aires which he had not seen since June, he would soon complete the bridge at Arroyo Ramallo – it all came pouring out in another lonely letter to Mary.

Then in January David's friend Bernard Culbard died. Deaths from disease or by accident were not uncommon, but this one particularly saddened David for he and Culbard had worked together in Brazil, sharing backwoods hardships and adventures for two years. Then they had found work together on the same railway line in Argentina: Culbard's base at Campana was eighty miles away, but David had often ridden there just for the pleasure of conversation and a smoke with a friend. Now he was gone, as David told Mary in another letter:

'Last Saturday night I had a telegram from San Pedro telling me that if I wished to see Culbard alive I must start at once as he was very ill. I started at once on horseback and we got there on Sunday forenoon, Powell accompanying me from Grant's camp. When we arrived we rode straight to the house and asked how Culbard was, the peon replying "El sta en el cemeterie", and they had gone burying him. He had died on Saturday night at 10.20 p.m. He had had dysentry for a week and it turned into inflammation of the bowel and peritonitis. His grave is in a lovely spot. They had to say he was a Catholic to get him into the cemetery at all. Poor fellow, he was telling me a week or two since that he intended to go home at the end of this job. We are going to put a headstone over him. Ask Tom to put this in the *Scotsman* for me: "Died at San Pedro, Rio Parana, on 3rd January, 1885, Bernard Culbard, Engineer on the Buenos Aires and Rosario Railway Extension." We have had a lot of deaths of late. On Tuesday we killed a Basque peon in an accident. He was a shunter. Yesterday another peon was drowned bathing. The weather is dreadfully hot, too, over 90 degrees Fahr. in the shade . . . '

Despite the sadness of Culbard's death, David himself never regretted the choice he had made to work in South America. Of course he was lonely without Mary, but even then he was constantly urging friends and relatives to follow his lead. There are many examples in letters home; this one concerned Mary's young brother Archie, who was now old enough to be looking for work:

'Your folks oughtn't to let Archie just take anything that "turns up", if that means putting him into an office. Give him either a profession or a trade. Here in South America the terms are synonymous and if anything a *trade* is the higher. The important man in this country is a good tradesman . . . I think it is disgraceful for anyone who is able to give a boy a chance in the world, to allow him (who knows no better) to get into some office where he may waste the best years of his life and turn out, even if successful, of little account. They can give him at least a fair chance to hold his own with the best, by sending him to a foundry or anywhere he may have a chance to learn something . . . If I had my life to live again I'd start at the planning bench and go through every stage of a foundry. At the age I am now I would have known more than I do or am ever likely to know. An engineer is the only profession besides medicine and science, worthy of the name, and it includes every sort of tradesman. There – I've got that off my chest. Do you know it has been haunting me the way that poor wretch Archie may be thrown away in some paltry office.' (In fact Archie became an electrical engineer but died in one of the first motor cycle accidents in Edinburgh.)

David's letters have left a vivid impression of his life in Argentina, and much of this story has been based on them, but for some reason almost all the letters from February to November 1885 are missing – probably destroyed intentionally. Members of the Angus family suspect that they may have reflected the strain which the long engagement and separation were placing on Mary and David, especially as Mary's mother and friends were urging her either to give him up or make him come back to stay in Britain, while he was just as keen to take her off to South America and the land of opportunity.

Despite his belief in the future of Argentina, David certainly made no secret of the difficulties in his work, the lack of 'society', the lurking prospect of revolutions, the sudden illnesses which carried off his friends and their wives. Perhaps it was a touch of conceit or bravado, perhaps just an ill-advised frankness, which made David describe these difficulties so openly to the girl he hoped to persuade to join him in South America. Whatever the reason, it had the opposite effect and it is no wonder that Mary's mother was thoroughly alarmed at the prospect of her daughter going off to such a wild place. A few letters from home refer to railway work in Australia – perhaps an attempt to steer David at least to a place in the British Empire, somewhere more familiar to people in Edinburgh.

Despite the problems in Argentina and in Scotland, David's railway line was completed in January 1886, and still stands, with the bridges, as a monument to his leadership and energies. However, as with the previous work in Brazil, the completion of the line left the engineers wondering what to do next. There were rumours of an extension to the Rosario line, but nothing definite materialised. There were always rumours, but they only served to raise false hopes. Then his old colleague Brotherhood wrote offering work on a harbour project in Brazil, but David turned it down because it would be too hot for Mary. Instead, he wrote of visiting Paraguay, which could be reached by using the same River Parana which he had been following on the Rosario railway work.

Only one thing was certain – David intended to come back to South America with Mary. The problem was to have a job ready to take up when he returned with his bride. But as the days passed and still no work turned up, frustration overtook him and in April David sailed home, still without a job.

Mary often told her daughters of David's home-coming in May 1886. They had not seen each other for four years, in fact they had hardly been alone with each other at all. Even Victorian conventions would have allowed them more time together, but Mary had gone off to teach in London just a week after their engagement, while David has been preoccupied making arrangements for Brazil. Even their final week together in London had been taken up largely by David's temporary job on the Kennington Oval tramline survey. That had been completed only hours before he left for Southampton. In some ways they hardly knew each other.

As the home-coming drew near, Mary found herself beset by all the old doubts and uncertainties which had preceded their engagement in 1882. She also feared that if she went off to South America, she would never see her ailing mother again. Was she even strong enough to face the rigours described so fully by David in his letters? As a result, she was genuinely nervous of meeting David again, lest they should both find that they had been mistaken about each other, and that, in spite of all their letters, they were strangers when they met. David, on the other hand, had no doubts at all. He never had any. He had waited four years and now he was coming home to Mary – it was as simple as that.

One of Mary's younger brothers went to meet him at the station. When she heard the cab driving up to the door, instead of running to meet him Mary rushed upstairs and hid behind the drawing room door. 'Where is she?' demanded David, bewildered by the fact that everyone but Mary was in the hall to meet him. He raced up the stairs and found her. Fifty years later Mary said of that meeting 'The minute he took me in his arms I knew it was all right, I knew we belonged to each other and I never doubted again.'

By now Mary was 28 and David nearly 31. For four years he had worked hard for his wedding, sending hundreds of pounds home to Mary as savings. Now he was back, a big, bronzed, fit and handsome man eager to be wed. Soon, however, he discovered, as many an impatient young lover had discovered before and since, that the law required him to wait three weeks while the banns were read. That was bad enough, but the young man also found that, for all his experiences of danger and adventure, he knew little of that formidable difficulty, the dreaded Victorian matron. Men may have imagined an importance as head of the household, but when Victorian women stood firm there was never any possibility of moving them. Mrs. Wilson and Mrs. Angus were about to do just that, for in their opinions David had returned at a most inconvenient time which did not suit them at all. The summer holidays were about to begin – both families had arranged to rent the same farmhouse on the island of Arran, the Anguses for the entire month of July, and the Wilsons for August, and neither family was willing to give up part of the letting to attend a wedding in Edinburgh! With astonishing selfishness the two familes, more exactly the two mothers, refused to have their holiday arrangements, or those of wedding guests, upset by David's eagerness to be married. Neither the Wilsons nor the Anguses could see any reason for the tearing hurry. The fact that David had waited four years already seemed to them good enough reason that he could wait a while longer. David, furious and frustrated as he was, was no match for the two strong-willed women. Mary meekly sided with her mother. David's father seems to have kept his head well down out of the cross-fire, and in the end David had no choice but to go along with the plans.

At this point David had still not obtained a job to go back to in South America. Although he was applying in all directions for work, he had to say on each application if he was prepared to go at once – but how could he, when he was not yet married? Not surprisingly he bercame bitter and frustrated, angry with everyone but Mary. In one letter to her from London, where he had gone for an interview, he wrote: 'I am beginning to think we'd better run away and put an end to all the troubles, for it is apparent that we cannot give satisfaction about the date to everybody – yet I suppose for this positively one and only occasion, *we* will be the *principal parties* in the affair, and our notions ought to have a little weight in the matter . . . '

There were many letters to and from London at this time, as David applied for jobs all over the world from China to Puerto Rica. He always hoped to go back to South America but as the weeks passed and still he found no work, a grumbly, dispirited David eventually joined his family on the island of Arran. For a moment he hoped that Mary might relent and join him there, but she stayed firmly by her mother's side, making the most of their last weeks together and preparing for the wedding. For a while he went through the motions of fishing and playing tennis with the others, but mostly he seems to have sat alone or gone wandering off over the hills which smother Arran – a 'walking funeral' as his brother George put it.

By now it had been decided that the wedding would be squeezed in between the two families' holidays. This was not a concession to David's wishes, but a decision made because it was found that the minister for the wedding, the celebrated Dr. Norman Macleod, would later be out of Edinburgh. The fact that Anne, Dowager Duchess of Athol, who had known Mrs. Wilson at Dunkeld, would also be passing through Edinburgh on her way to Balmoral for a period as Lady-in-Waiting to Queen Victoria, may also have helped Mrs. Wilson to change her mind about the date.

By now the wedding presents had also begun to accumulate. They made a very Victorian list – silver jelly holders, a table egg-boiler used with a spirit lamp, a set of silver salt dishes and the like, and '. . . Aunt Annie sent me this morning a pair of silk socks she has knitted me to wear at the wedding. That is two pairs now, I hope no more folks will go in for knitting special socks for the occasion or I'll have to have a special pair of boots made.'

The night before her wedding, Mary's mother gave her two pieces of advice. What Mary knew about the physical side of marriage had come from the maids in the Dunkeld Manse, from her knowledge of farm animals, and perhaps a little from the physiology and anatomy she had studied at London (though even textbooks skirted sexual matters with great skill), but even now Mrs. Wilson's advice was quite different. Quoting from the Bible, she said 'Never let the sun go down on your wrath', in other words, always make up your differences before you go to sleep, and don't let anger and resentment grow between you. Then she said, 'Mary, no matter how much you may be surprised or even frightened by what marriage means, never let your husband see your reluctance or nervousness or distaste, for men are very sensitive about these things.' This must have been a little disconcerting for the blushing bride, but in fact Mary's marriage was very different from her mother's, and once she was married there were no difficulties. She and David were so happily matched and so genuinely in love, that in spite of all the changes and chances in life, the thirteen children they would have, the good times and the bad, they remained as David so often signed himself, devoted lovers to their lives' end.

The next day, which was also David's 31st birthday, the marriage went off without a hitch. The ceremony was held in the drawing room of 18 Warriston Crescent, as was the custom in these days for Protestants in Scotland. A service in church would have been considered rather *papist*! It took place in the afternoon, followed by afternoon tea and carriages at 5 o'clock. Both Mrs. Wilson and Mrs. Angus were teetotal so there was no drink. Nevertheless, a great crowd of relatives from both sides came, and the room must have been very full. The Dowager Duchess of Athol turned up, and the minister agreed to delay his departure for two days to let him officiate, so the event was a great success. The only critical note came in a letter from David's father, where he wrote in a postscript, 'has Mary recovered from the fatigue of that confoundedly long ceremony? If *length* may help, your knot is tied siccarly enough!'

Then David and Mary set off on their honeymoon. Their years of waiting were over as they now caught the train to Forres, where David's favourite aunt Miss Anne Stewart was staying at the Hydropathic Hotel taking the cure. Miss Stewart often stayed at this hotel and was quite a well-known character there but this time she had told everyone that her nephew was bringing his bride to see her straight from their wedding. Poor Mary! From the moment she arrived she realised that everyone knew they were newly-weds. Worse still, they were housed in a temporary annex to the main hotel, where the walls were very thin – since they could hear every word and movement in the next room, they hardly dared speak to each other themselves either. Years later Mary confessed that it was the most embarrassing time in her life.

From Forres David took Mary to see his boyhood home in Findhorn and to meet old friends there. They went on walks and explored many of his old haunts before continuing on by steamer through the Caledonian Canal to Fort William, and from there on to Arran where the Wilsons now occupied the holiday farmhouse. Craw Farm stood on a hillside a couple of miles from Lochranza at the north end of Arran, with beautiful views across the Kilbrannan Sound towards the hills of Kintyre – some of the finest scenery in Scotland, and an idyllic place for a honeymoon in August. They also had the use of a horse and trap and the farm's own boat. This time it was a much happier David Angus who fished and played tennis and wandered over the hills with Mary looking for sprigs of lucky white heather.

Finally they left the island and visited David's family at Langside in Glasgow. David's oldest brother James now lived in San Francisco but his other brothers and sister Isa were there to meet him – perhaps the last time when so many of them were together at once.

David also threw himself into many applications for work that autumn, but nothing resulted. They had almost decided to go off to Buenos Aires and look for work there on the spot, when Mrs. Wilson's great friends the Buchanans offered David an unexpected job in the Argentine, beginning as soon as he could get there. He was to survey some land owned by the Buchanans near Monte Cuman in the foothills of the Andes Mountains. This survey was seen as a preliminary to later developing the property if it proved promising. This, in turn, would mean a more-or-less permanent job for David managing the estate. David and Mary were delighted at the unexpected change of fortune, particularly since Mary now knew that she was pregnant. Just in time, the future seemed secure.

Before leaving, Mary and her mother went on a shopping spree round all the best Edinburgh shops. First they went to an exclusive French shop in Princes Street, where they bought one of each type of garment the baby was expected to need, and yards of handkerchief lawn and fine flannel and ounces of white 'fingering' as knitting wool and then called, so that Mary could complete more embroidered shifts and petticoats, barracoats and dresses on the voyage out to Argentina.

At Bessemer's in Princes Street, where they specialised in fitting people out for the tropics, they took more advice on what a baby would need in a hot climate, but no-one, not even Mrs. Ryan who had lived for years in Ceylon, thought to tell Mary what *she* would need as a pregnant woman. David does not seem to have been consulted, for this was women's business; the result was that Mary went off with a completely unsuitable wardrobe of very Scottish clothes which were no use at all in South America. For example, she had been married in a dress of natural coloured camel-hair material, with a jabot of silk and lace at the neck. She had also worn this as her going-away dress, for it was so very becoming, but like the rest of her trousseau it proved useless in Argentina since it could not be altered to suit her growing figure, and the material was too heavy. When she reached the tropics Mary found that the only dress she had cool enough for the heat was a cotton 'wrapper' which her mother had suggested would do as an overall when she was cooking!

Mrs. Wilson and Mary's brother Tom went down to Southampton to see the couple off. It was the farthest Mrs. Wilson had ever travelled in her life, almost as if she knew that she would never see her daughter again. Perhaps David, for all his faults in her eyes, had reassured her that *could* take care of Mary, but maybe even to the end Mrs. Wilson worried about the young man who was whisking her daughter off to Argentina. As Mary feared, she never did see her mother again. David never saw his parents again either, for his father died of cancer in 1889 and his mother died in 1890, before they had time to return to Scotland.

Chapter Five

THE FOOTHILLS OF THE ANDES 1886-1887

On December 4th, 1886 the S.S. *Leibnitz* finally brought the Anguses to Buenos Aires. They were met on the jetty by Mrs. Henderson, a Scots woman who ran a boarding house in town. Another friend also turned up to steer them quickly through the customs. It must have relieved Mary to find that there were people around who so obviously knew and liked her husband; she would not be alone in Buenos Aires when David went off to survey for the Buchanans.

On the voyage Mary had befriended another female passenger who was bringing her five children out to their father in Argentina. Once ashore, the first priority was to find a hotel for this family, which Mrs. Henderson did in fluent Spanish while Mary trailed along behind. She thought that she would have to stay at the same hotel, for David had already rushed off to meet people and make arrangements for his survey at Monte Cuman, but Mrs. Henderson had taken a liking to Mary and offered accommodation at her boarding house. Normally she forbade females in her establishment, which was used to many young bachelor engineers and businessmen working or seeking work in Buenos Aires, but she waived this rule for Mary and offered to let her stay, not only while David was away surveying, but until the baby was born. From that first day in South America, Mrs. Henderson became a friend and great support to Mary.

The next day Mary sent her first letter home, and already she was full of wide-eyed colour and description. Although she was relieved to find other Europeans and signs of a familiar way of life, and had quickly converted their own rooms to something 'quite homelike with the Dunkeld photographs and the travelling clock and all David's books out,' in common with David she never felt lost in a strange place and she soon settled in. Even her first night's experience of mosquitos was described more in tones of curious news than of distaste:

'Yesterday (their day of arrival) we went to the Scotch church and had a very nice service, but it was very hot. Each pew is provided with a fan like the Japanese straw ones in the drawing room at home. All the ladies fanned themselves throughout the service and I was very glad to make use of one too. We were introduced to Mr. Fleming, the minister . . . Then Mrs. Henderson took us back to lunch and it was then she told us that she will take us as boarders. I am very glad to be among people whom David knows and they seem such downright, plain, good Scots people. We had a delightful tea there too, bread and butter, cheese and home-made cake. It is quite true that the butter is churned on the way in to town by jogging on the horse's back . . . We did not get much sleep owing to the fleas and mosquitos, but not all the insects are bad, we saw some beautiful fireflies at Belgrano. All David's friends seem to be kind people and I shall be quite spoiled unless somebody begins to scold me soon. I have had a busy day opening boxes and getting things out, and altering my pink print dress, which I hope to wear tomorrow . . . The cholera seems to be confined to the parts by the river, but as a precaution against it people are fined for selling fruit, and all milk and water has to be boiled before it is drunk. The streets are very narrow and badly paved but they do seem to be trying to improve them, to judge by the turned up state of some of them just now . . . Mrs. Henderson's house is in an open square, principally on one storey. All the houses are built round a square called the patio with shrubs growing in it, and all the rooms have long glass windows, opening into the patio which makes them very airy. We are to have two nice rooms, opening into each other, and with windows looking into the public square which is laid out with gardens and fountains. I will have my meals with the family but will always have my own sitting room to sit in . . .'

David had planned to leave for Monte Cuman on December 20th, barely a fortnight after reaching Buenos Aires, so he was busy organising tickets, provisions and equipment, and could not always be with Mary. She, on the other hand, was now plunged into the social round of British families in the city, delivering letters, parcels or just messages from friends in Scotland, or entertaining David's friends who dropped in while he was out. It must have been quite a difficult time for Mary, bewildered in a strange place, being hustled around by well-meaning friends of David's in an attempt to make her feel at home, and so anxious to create a good impression for her husband's sake. She had to adapt quickly to a different language, to new foods cooked in unusual local ways, and to those unwritten nuances of manners and customs which can beset anyone in another land. She came through it all with flying colours simply by being herself, as in the comment on the Carmen Miranda hats worn by everyone who was anyone in the city: 'The fashion of ladies' hats here is astonishing. They are from 18 to 20 inches high and are decked out with regular flower gardens perched high above the straw. My hat is a pigsty beside them, and I am glad it is.'

Finally the day came when David had to leave for the interior. By now he had found a Norwegian friend called Worsoe to help him on the survey but it was with some trepidation that they prepared for their work, for they now learned that they would have to journey through an area around the town of Mendoza where a cholera epidemic was raging.

Mary, a natural worrier at the best of times, fretted terribly at the thought of cholera. No amount of reassurance from David seemed to calm her, and in the end he had to leave her still upset and anxious. Mary, pregnant in an unfamiliar world, with Christmas and its thoughts of Scotland just a week away, watched her husband leave for an area reputedly infested with cholera to undertake a survey upon which their future hung – it must have been an awful moment.

On the day before leaving David took Mary to church. Then next day, with last minute preparations completed, he made his farewells at Mrs. Henderson's house and with Worsoe caught a train to Mendoza. It took two days for the train to hiss and rattle slowly across the plains towards the Andes mountains – Mendoza was as far as the train could go across the pampa for at that time there was still no line across the mountains. From Mendoza, David's plan was to travel several days southwards to the small town of San Rafael, the closest place to the remote estate of Monte Cuman which he was to survey.

As David and Worsoe journeyed west to Mendoza rumours about the cholera grew stronger, and at one point the train actually stopped. Only the presence of some government officials on board persuaded the engine driver to continue on into the epidemic area. Eventually David reached San Vicente, a village six miles outside Mendoza, where he and Worsoe left the train. Talk of the cholera was everywhere – the latest count was over 200 cases and 31 deaths in the town. This was perhaps not surprising, for the drains were no more than open sewers. Some people thought David was a doctor and tried to stop him in the street – not knowing that his own protection against cholera was little more than a glass of Eno's Fruit Salts! Surprisingly there was a telegraph office at San Vicente and David was at last able to contact Mary, as she wrote later to her mother:

'I have been very anxious all week about David, but yesterday afternoon I got a telegram from San Vicente, a village about six miles south of Mendoza, which is almost depopulated by cholera. The newspaper accounts every day are dreadful, people dying after only an hour or two's illness. I wish David were safe back: I cannot tell you how thankful I was for yesterday's telegram – I had not heard since he left five days ago. I don't suppose I shall hear above once or twice till he is on his way back, but they have plenty of cholera remedies with them so we can only trust that they will get safe through. Poor David, he won't have a very bright Christmas in the coach on the way to San Rafael. There was no use in his going to Mendoza just now to see the lawyers and so on, for all who possibly could have fled the town . . .'

Although San Vincente was largely deserted, David eventually found and hired three peons, or local men, called José, Luigi and Gonzales. On Christmas Day 1886 a procession of 20 mules, a covered cart, the three peons, David and Worsoe finally set off soutwards for Monte Cuman. They travelled mostly over scrub, through small peasant villages with Spanish names where they tried to buy food and water. There was the compensating view of the magnificent snow-capped Andes to the west, but David's diary vividly describes the frustrations and difficulties of that lumbering wagon journey:

'*Dec. 26th:* (The peons had gone on ahead with the cart) Started at 11.10 and drove into Trio Esquinas 1.30. Found cart in front of a house where cholera was. Sent for mules and went forward five squares to the potrero (clover meadow) put out beds under big willow trees and had siesta. Sent peon José back for water which he took from Asequia. Sent him back for *well* water and made tea. Luigi and José went for provisions – now we have 3 hens and a dozen eggs. Started about 4.30 p.m. and got to El Balda about 8 o'clock. Had dinner with some villainous looking ruffians and started again at 11.30. Went till one in the morning when we unsaddled and went to sleep on our camp beds in the open – the country is desert – sand and scrub – from three leagues beyond Trio Esquinas.

'*Dec. 27th:* Started at 5 in the morning after drinking tea and some half baked criolla bread – horrible stuff like half made biscuits. Rode about 3 leagues and stopped for ten minutes to drink wine – ate more criolla bread – then on again for seven more leagues to Totoral at 1 o'clock, when we had sapa, puchiro, and asado – same horrible bread – siesta for 3 hours when it began to rain. We slept below the cart and the peons outside . . . Gonzales is ill with pains in the stomach. Started again at 5 o'clock. Worsoe and I went in the cart and got to San Carlos at 9 o'clock – 5 leagues – it was quite dark when we arrived and no-one would let us in. W and I slept in the cart, the others under it. Rained very hard at night. We put up in a street off the plaza. The town is an old one but the streets are very bad . . . Some apple trees. Poplars all the way. Mendoza to San Carlos 30 leagues.

'*Dec. 28th:* Gonzales still ill – sent Luigi to order breakfast at the porida – W and I went thro' the town – tried to get a lamp but could not. Arranged to buy some carne and arroz before leaving – had breakfast, very poor one. Gonzales took a little soup. Went to telegraph office, but could not send a message as line is not open till 1/1/87. Siesta and wrote diary. José went for mules at 2.50 p.m. Started 3.30 p.m. Gonzales very ill, gave him some chlorodyne. 10 cents per head per night for the mules. (At this point Gonzales was apparently left behind at a house, indicated by later diary references). Arrived Bellavista (5 leagues from San Carlos) at 8.30 p.m. Stayed in the house of Don Stiago and had dinner . . .'

One advantage to travelling around inland South America was that local landowners always welcomed the opportunity of educated conversation over dinner, and often offered overnight accommodation. Life was usually so dull away from the cities – a fact which more than once produced meat, drink and a bed for David on his travels in remote areas.

Eventually the party reached the outskirts of the tiny town of San Raphael 'where we were stopped by a soldier who put up a white cloth on a pole to call the doctor. We waited till 5.30 but sent letter to Dioclesias Garcia (David's contact) by boy, paying him 20 cents. A sargeant came and examined us, then took us to a tumbledown looking rancho where we were fumigated with sulphur. Our clothes had to be taken off and fumigated and we washed in fenic acid (sic) and water . . .'

A post left San Rafael once a week and David was able to tell Mary that he had passed safely through the cholera region. Their separation must have been a wrench for both Mary and David, but he was the more demonstrative in his letters:

'I am very sorry to be away from you today – before we were married I used to think that I could not do without you, now I *know* it. I am not sure whether you may not be ill yourself, you must be careful of yourself and not get cholera. I don't know what I would do if anything happened to you, it is bad enough being away from you at all, and if I had not the outlook of getting back in a month or so, it would be unbearable. I am very sorry to have had to leave you at this time, but it is the fear of the poor house and I would be earning nothing in Buenos Aires just now, but I'd rather be with you . . . You are my very *life* – though I hope for all things we are still at the foot of the ladder, and our grand castles are still in the air as yet. However I'll try hard to bring them down soon to *terra firma,* even though we have to start in a ranch, lass, and you would make a palace of a ranch. You are my fortune, and success or failure of other things is a secondary matter to me, except in so far that I will be able to get more for you and to show you more strongly *how I love you . . .*' (to which Mary answered with a rather prim little sentence 'I am glad you miss me a little too'.)

The estate of Monte Cuman turned out to be a run-down looking *estancia* surrounded by the simple willow houses of about 300 natives, none of whom could read or write. The impoverished villagers kept horses, goats and sheep, which they protected from wild animals lurking in the algarobe forests nearby. In one letter David wrote that 'two of the villagers were eaten by tigers lately, pumas really; there are also foxes, ostriches and deer, hares and all kinds of game.' Some of the locals hunted with a three-ball bolas: 'He throws it at the animal he is going for and the balls spread away until the rope strikes, when they curl round the victim, and it curls up too . . .'

Beyond the village stretched an indeterminate area of open scrub land, mostly trees and shrubs with little grass except beside streams. The entire area was hemmed into the angle formed by two rivers, the Atuel and the Diamante – David's job was to explore and survey this land, particularly for its potential as a farming area for settlers. The 1880's was a period of great emigration from Europe (between 1850 and 1880 the population of Argentina doubled, and it doubled again in the next thirty years). The Buchanans clearly hoped to attract tenants to their estate, employing David as their general manager.

For the next few weeks David and Worsoe lived in their covered wagon out on the *camp,* surveying and measuring the land. Until recently this had been Indian territory: 'On Tuesday night we slept in the house of a French surveyor named Ballofet, who lives in a large mud fort which he built 18 years ago when he first came here. It had a moat and a drawbridge and a portcullis – but it is now 8 years since the Indians made their last raid and they are now a thousand miles south of this.' Now the people were mostly Chilean peasants, very poor and simple farmers – David's work included plotting their villages and irrigation channels on a map, and estimating the *real* potential of the land. He evidently saw hope in it, for he wrote to Mary: 'The ground is rather bare, only thorn bushes except where water has been brought: then wheat, barley and maize will grow and it looks like harvest fields at home. Some of the people have small flower and kitchen gardens and trees are being planted. In a few years time the place will bear a very different appearance, and there will be railways in a year or two . . .'

It was nevertheless a difficult survey. The weather was very hot, and David, a big heavy man, perspired terribly. The nights were, by contrast, bitterly cold, and the chilly ground forced them to rise early each morning – generally by 4.30 or 5 o'clock. By six, when it was not yet hot, they were at work and continued on to about 11.30 when they normally paused for breakfast and a two hour siesta under the wagon. Then they worked on to 7.30 and by nine o'clock the weary men were all asleep.

Most of the work was among spikey bushes which scraped the skin and snagged the clothes: 'All the trees and bushes here have very bad thorns and I have ruined one pair of flannel trousers, my riding breeches, my coat, helmet and nearly all my handkerchiefs. I have to use them for flags for marking out bushes. We don't get much washing here, but Worsoe and I bathe in the river which keeps us moderately clean, and we are healthy and strong as horses . . .'

David could only obtain two peons as assistants, so that even a simple job such as planting a marker pole could take hours. In the end David and Worsoe did most work themselves, pacing out levels and distances through the thorn bushes each day. Measurements were made with a cow-hide rope. The speed of rivers and streams was estimated by timing a piece of wood floating on the current. Away from the stream, thirst was a constant problem as in this diary note: '. . . where we got water, both ourselves and our horses being nearly dead broke for want of water.' Eventually David bought a goat and made a water bag from the skin.

Here and there David and Worsoe encountered native settlements, where they bought food. For a few days their normal diet of beef and brick-hard doughy bread would be replaced by mutton, potatoes, onions, pumpkins and lots of fresh milk, before dwindling back to the beef and indigestible bread again. Occasionally they were able to buy eggs, which they usually boiled early in the morning as a snack before setting off into the bushes for the day's first measuring.

Part of the Buchanan lands seem to have stretched into the Andeas foothills, but by the time David set off to tackle this area even he was beginning to feel tired, as in this comment to his Buchanan patrons: 'It is rather rough work and living here, and you must excuse this rambling letter. It is written in our cart, the ink is nearly dry in the bottle, and I am very sore from riding – I have gone over 700 miles on horse or mule back in the last month . . .'

At one place David found a number of petroleum springs, where the crude oil actually bubbled out of the ground and trickled off down the hillside in little streams. David described them in a letter to his younger brother George: 'Away up in the mountains we found a petroleum well about 2 metres in diameter and 1 metre deep, full of hot pitch and oil and the whole hillside was black, sticky and soft with a general pervading odour of sulphur and brimstone. Small birds and beasts get caught up in it. At the foot of the hill a small stream of petroleum runs away just like a stream of water. It is a wonderful place.'

In Scotland, James 'Paraffin' Young had been pioneering the refining of oil for twenty years (and had made a fortune by selling his method of distillation to the Americans), but David does not seem to have been aware of the commercial possibilities of the oil field he had found, and regarded the pools more as natural curiosities.

David may have overlooked the oil, but he was nevertheless convinced that the Monte Cuman property could be developed. He himself bought some land close by as a speculative investment, and now he also made a preliminary survey of the land to San Luis, about 250 miles to the north, beyond Mendoza, looking at the best route for a railway to San Rafael. This would bring the big city populations within reach of Monte Cuman and make farming a more realistic possibility.

In February David completed his survey for the Buchanans and thankfully returned to Mary in Buenos Aires. The field notebooks and diaries of his survey survive but the full report has been lost. However, he certainly recommended that the land should be developed, and seems to have suggested digging irrigation channels across the estate from the Atuel and Diamante rivers. Unfortunately a lawsuit now began over the precise extent of the Monte Cuman lands and the Buchanans in Scotland had second thoughts. David's scheme was costly, they said, and there were now suddenly several infant heirs in the family. In the end they shelved the plan, and David was never offered the post of manager.

Ten years later when the legal dust had settled the Buchanans commissioned a new survey. By now David was busy elsewhere and another surveyor did the work. Then a brochure was published to attract immigrants to Monte Cuman. The railway had now reached San Rafael and farming had become a more commercial proposal. Today the area is well populated, the oil wells are in production, the rivers have been dammed to catch the spring melt-water from the Andes, and irrigation channels allow farmers to grow wheat, cotton and grapes and to rear cattle – much as David foresaw in 1887.

Meanwhile David returned to a joyous reunion with Mary. Now they could look forward to the birth of their first child, albeit over-shadowed by the fact that, for the moment, David had no work. He and Mary still expected to live at Monte Cuman, not knowing yet that their hopes would be dashed; meanwhile he applied for temporary jobs to tide him over until they left for the Buchanan lands.

At this moment David's former employers Prebble and Ware, who had the concession for the Great Southern Railway, were planning a line beyond Rosario to Sante Fé and Cordoba. For a short time David was employed to survey a rail head on the River Parana, but all too soon the plans for a jetty at Las Piedras were completed and David's contract ended. Later he 'made preliminary surveys, prepared plans, estimates and necessary documents for securing concessions for a railway from San Nicolas to Trenque Lauquen' as his *curriculum vitae* on other applications for work later recorded. He also surveyed and planned a rural tramway for San Nicolas and district, and David's delightful sketches and plans of the country stations and tiny locomotives intended for this line still survive. These were all very short jobs, but the income was enough to tide the Anguses over.

On May 11th the baby was born. To begin with the midwife

arrived a month too early and had to be sent home again. When she was eventually sent for at the correct time, she was determined not to call in the doctor in charge of the case – if she managed on her own she could claim a double fee – but for Mary it meant a difficult first birth. The midwife insisted that all was well, but when the doctor was at last fetched the poor young mother needed a good many stitches. However, at the end of it all David and Mary were the proud parents of a son. He was christened David after his father and great-grandfather, a very Scottish habit, but to distinguish father from son he was known as Davie-lad.

Though he kept a respectful Victorian father's safe distance from the sight of nappies and 'woman's work', David clearly enjoyed the new role of fussing husband and proud father. The baby evidently had 'David's forehead and his hair goes into a peak at the front just like David's' – though in the one case the hair was on its way in, while in the other it was on its way out! Soon Mary was describing her life with the new arrival to her mother:

'He gives me plenty to do during the day, but he is sleeping better at night and only wakes once or twice hunting for his milk. This is how we manage. I rise at 7.00 a.m. and make a nice cup of tea in Mrs. Ryan's pot, we drink it out of Miss Wark's cups, stir it with Mrs. Ryan's spoons and take the tea out of Janie's tea-caddy and the sugar from the Dunmore sugar basin. So you can see many of our old friends help us with our cup of refreshing! Our lamp burns all night and keeps the water hot. Mrs. Henderson comes down the patio soon after 7.00 to see how we have passed the night and she has a cup of tea with us and bread and butter. That meal over, David amuses the baby till I dress, but I don't often get further than my upper petticoat before I have to take the infant and begin his washing preparations, while David lies in his bed and superintends with a critical eye. The crater is very happy with his bath and spreads himself out to enjoy himself, but doesn't he lift up his voice when I take him out! Fortunately he is not a very sliddery kind of baby, but solid and firm, so I have had no accident in the way of drowning him yet!

In another letter soon after she added:

'I wish you could see the baby. He is noticing a great deal now, everything he sees is a wonder to him. He lies and stares and laughs at a strip of bright yellow flannel we pin up on the bed curtain . . . Mrs. Henderson and I went into town and bought a nice swinging bassinette perambulator for him, it is dark brown and almost the same as we had at Dunkeld for Hughie . . .'

The last few lines of this letter are badly blotched as if with tears, but whether they were Mary's homesick ones or her mother's cannot be told. The letters themselves are timeless and might have been written by any homesick young mother longing to show off her baby to her family.

For years David had been urging others in the Wilson and Angus families to join him in South America. To begin with there was some hesitation for some of his descriptions were certainly of rough places, but the birth of Davie-lad added more incentive. For a time Mrs. Wilson herself toyed with the idea of emigrating (her mother had left Scotland for Australia in middle age) but the first to take the plunge was Mary's brother Tom. He was a sickly youth and hoped for a better climate in Argentina, but like everyone else he also dreamed of making his fortune there. At first he only found a rather badly paid job as a clerk in an office of the Rosario Railway, at 60 dollars a month until he became fluent in Spanish. But it was a beginning and meanwhile he started Spanish lessons.

Undoubtedly Mary was overjoyed to see her brother, who seems now to have lived with them in Mrs. Henderson's boarding house, but unfortunately he was a terrible pessimist and invariably depressed her whenever David was away looking for work. By now the Angus finances were very low indeed; there was a fear that they would even have to leave Mrs. Henderson's house for somewhere cheaper, which particularly worried Mary. By now they had heard of the Buchanans' legal problems and realised that David might not be given work at Monte Cuman after all. The last thing Mary needed now was Tom's despondant talk while the more optimistic David was away.

As a result of all this David's search for work took him increasingly further afield. He even applied for two railway concessions, for which he would have needed to raise capital and form companies. Nothing came of these schemes, perhaps for the best. More realistic was the possibility of work in nearby Uruguay. Like Argentina, this country was also expanding during the 1880's. Some railways had already been built, mostly by British companies, but progress had not been so spectacular as in Argentina because fewer immigrants had settled in Uruguay. Even at this time most people still lived in or around the city of Montevideo, just across the estuary of the River Plate from Buenos Aires. For David it was a simple matter to catch a boat across the wide river mouth and after several fruitless visits this brought some modest results.

David was commissioned to design a jetty and lighthouse for Montevideo harbour. Perhaps his Stevenson experience counted here, for the Scottish firm was now enjoying a world-wide reputation and David's training had certainly been thorough. This work gained David a foot-hold in Uruguay, but unfortunately his designs were soon completed – he appears to have drawn the plans only, and not to have supervised the actual building work. Nevertheless it was a start. The jetty and lighthouse even featured briefly but prominently in news films of the scuttling of the German battleship *Graf Spee* at Montevideo in 1939, and they still stand today.

Soon David was back in Uruguay looking for more work. He was even there on his 32nd birthday, their first wedding anniversary, but it proved to be a lucky day, for on it was signed the contract appointing him to take full charge of a survey for the Midland Uruguay Railway from Las Toros on the Rio Negro to the town of Salto. The company sent him straight away to make a preliminary 'flying survey' (apparently for no salary, on the understanding that if the line proved feasable he would be put in charge of a more detailed survey). Meanwhile he also tried to find somewhere to live with Mary, for it seemed that their destiny now lay in Uruguay. All this time, however the Angus savings were rapidly dwindling to nothing.

David managed to sell the speculative plot of land he had bought at Monte Cuman and this kept them going for a few more weeks, but things were soon desperate again. (David nearly always bought small plots of land near where he was working: after his death in 1926 it took his family 5 years to unravel all his dealings.) Meanwhile on August 21st Mary wrote to David, who was still in Uruguay:

'I don't know whether you will be displeased with me or not, but I got Tom to present your signed cheque at the bank to bring me 70 m/n gold. Actually I got 90.30 m/n for it . . . as you had only signed one cheque I had to get it all out at once. Now you have only got 30.00 m/n gold left in your bank. The reason was that Tom paid D.D.H. the 20.00 m/n which you owed him, and so Tom had not enough to pay his Spanish teacher on Monday. I have paid Tom the 20.00 m/n, and after paying Mrs. Henderson and for Nestles milk, fuller's earth, mending cotton etc. etc. *I have only 13.00 m/n left.*'

A few days later David returned unexpectedly early. He had called to see his employers at Montevideo on the way back from the flying survey, but Mary was not expecting him so soon. She was bathing the baby one morning when she heard his footsteps on the patio outside. He came in glowing with excitement and cried out, 'Mary hold out your lap.' She put down the baby on the bed and held out the corners of her apron. Into it David poured a hundred golden dollars like a stream of gold. Mary gasped at the miracle – she always used that word to describe this, the first of a series of such incidents in their fluctuating fortunes. It was an advance on David's first month's salary. Their luck had turned.

David Angus with his father in 1859.

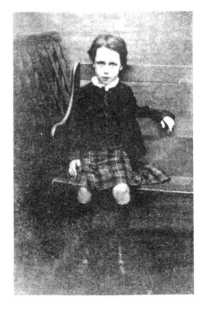

David Angus aged 7 or 8. He was a boarder at Cauvins Hospital, Edinburgh until 1865.

Cauvins Hospital,
Jany 7th 1865.

My dear Mother,
        I received James's kind letter and the picture in it. I was happy to hear that you are quite well. I wish all friends a very happy New Year. I enjoyed myself exceedingly during the happy season. We had a football match on cristmas day and a party

One of Davids' letters to his mother. This one describing the Christmas of 1864 at Cauvins.

David with his mother, Betsy Stewart Angus, taken in 1865 when David was aged ten. The photograph was taken in Forres during the years they lived at Findhorn.

David's parents, William Angus and Betsy Stewart Angus, about 1886.

David and Mary Angus
photographed on their honeymoon.
They were married on 29th July
1886.

1892. David Angus and Mary Angus with three of their children, baby Betty,
Nancy and Stewart with David Angus. Picture taken just after the nurse
joined and just before the family went to Chile.

A drawing from the Angus notebooks.

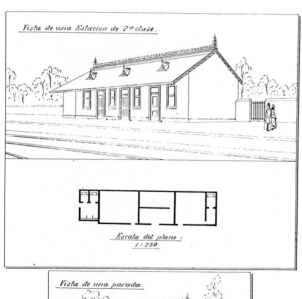

Station building and shelter from San Nicolas, Argentina, taken from the notebooks of David Angus.

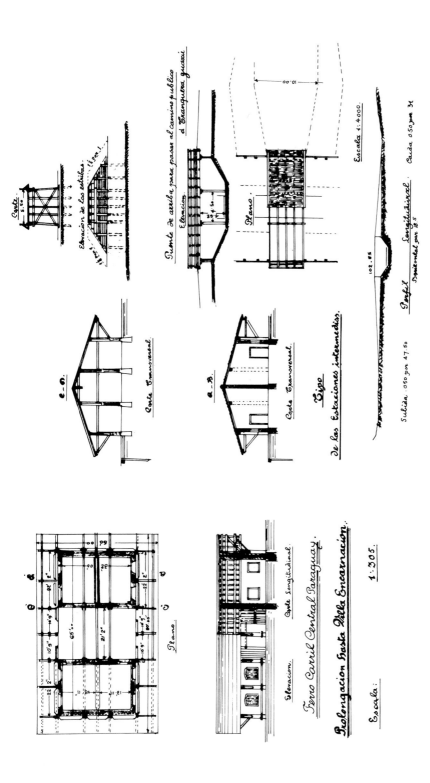

Pages from the notebooks of David Angus 1887. (Traced by H.M. Baker 1977).

The Hernandaria bridge, Paraguay. These two
photographs show the same train before and after the
bridge collapsed January 1891.

A Christmas party in Villa Rica, Paraguay, probably 1889, David Angus right at the back, balding with moustache, between the two lanterns.

Digging a cutting for the railway in Paraguay.

The opening of the line in Paraguay August 1891. Fourth from the right at the front is Dr Stewart, the President of Paraguay, on his right is David Angus with the slightly squashed hat.

A picnic in Paraguay, 1890. Mary Angus standing centre holding baby Stewart.

David Angus and party mounted on bullocks while surveying in Damaraland, Southern Africa. November 1892.

David Angus' staff and colleagues at Colico, Chile.

Chile. The railway station at Coronel. The Angus family lived in the large flat above the station.

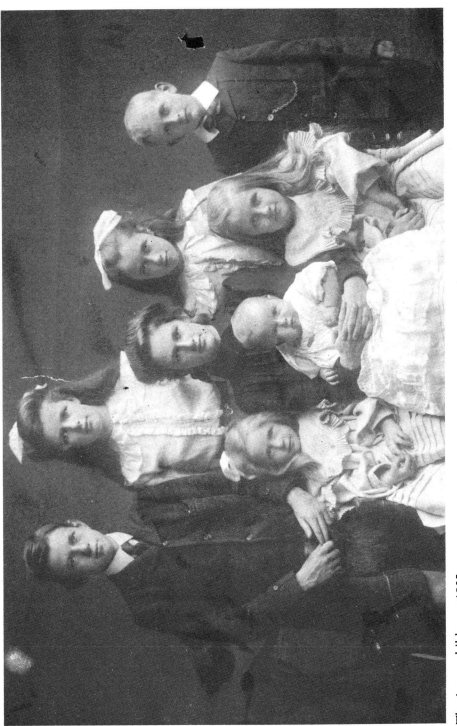

The Angus children c. 1905.

There were many dangers for the Angus family to face in Chile, including 'bandidos'. The group shown here were captured while they lay in wait for the paymaster 'up the line'. Note the sawn-off rifles called 'chocos'. It is believed that the group were all hanged.

The station at Colico, Chile. David Angus, centre, with some of his colleagues.

David Angus, centre, on horseback. On the right is Manuel who taught the children to ride and keep the stables.

Nancy, aged 8 and Betty, aged 4. Photograph taken in Chile in 1896.

Archie Angus in 1902. He was born at Colico, Chile in 1897. Died Messines, France 1914.

Don Luis Izquierdo, taken in 1907. He was a guest of the Angus family when Louie was christened and he acted as a godfather. He was later to become President of Chile.

The Arauco coal mine in Chile.

1906. Earthquake damage in Valparaiso, Chile. Coronel was shaken by the same earthquake as was, more famously, San Francisco in California.

A view of Coronel harbour, Chile.

A view of the south end of the Bio-Bio bridge, Chile. This bridge was swept away in a flood and David Angus had it rebuilt. The earlier bridge, like the first Tay bridge had thick piers against which rubbish, trees etc collected. The water gained force and carried the piers away. This new bridge had lighter piers through which the water could flow more easily.

Stewart Angus. Picture taken December 1897 when he was aged 7. He was killed on the Somme on 1st July 1916.

David Angus in 1917. At this time he was preparing for a trip to Serbia which he never made.

Mary Wilson Angus in 1905.

Stewart and Nancy Angus c.1900. Preparing to travel home to Britain with their aunt Georgie Wilson to attend boarding school. Nancy's dress is preserved in a costume museum in Gloucestershire.

The Angus grave in Marylebone Cemetery, Finchley, North London.

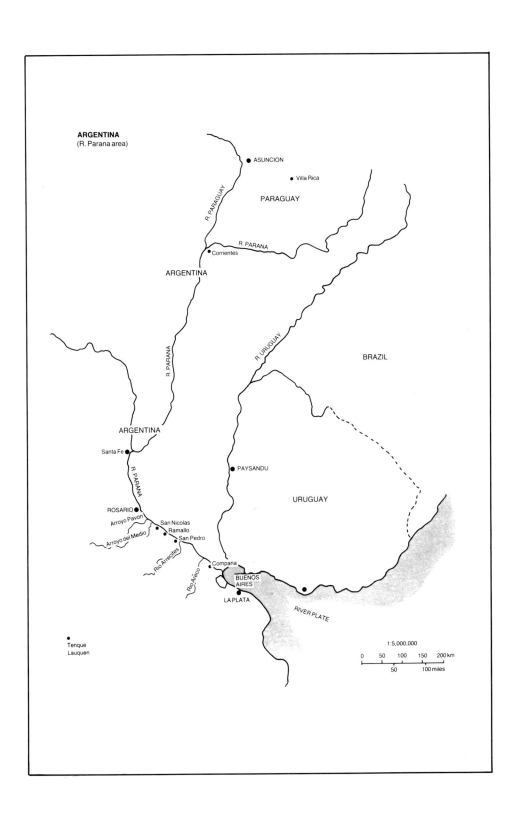

ARGENTINA
(R. Parana area)

ASUNCION

Villa Rica

PARAGUAY

R. PARAGUAY

R. PARANA

Corrientes

ARGENTINA

R. PARANA

R. URUGUAY

BRAZIL

ARGENTINA

Santa Fe

PAYSANDU

URUGUAY

R. PARANA

ROSARIO

Arroyo Pavon

San Nicolas

Ramallo

Arroyo del Medio

San Pedro

Rio Arrecifes

Compana

Rio Añeco

BUENOS
AIRES

LA PLATA

RIVER PLATE

Tenque
Lauquen

1:5,000,000

0   50   100   150   200 km

50   100 miles

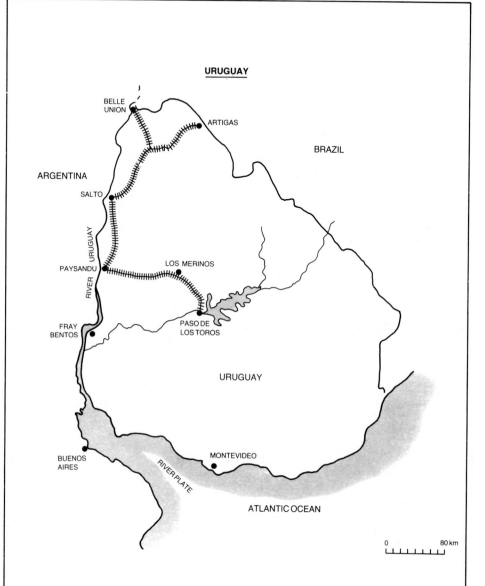

URUGUAY

ARGENTINA

BELLE UNION

ARTIGAS

BRAZIL

SALTO

RIVER URUGUAY

PAYSANDU

LOS MERINOS

FRAY BENTOS

PASO DE LOS TOROS

URUGUAY

BUENOS AIRES

RIVER PLATE

MONTEVIDEO

ATLANTIC OCEAN

0   80 km

NOTE: THE ONLY RAILWAY SHOWN IS THE ONE CONNECTED WITH DAVID ANGUS. HE SURVEYED THE ENTIRE LENGTH, AND CONSTRUCTED THE SECTION FROM PASO DE LOS TOROS, THROUGH PAYSANDU, TO SALTO.

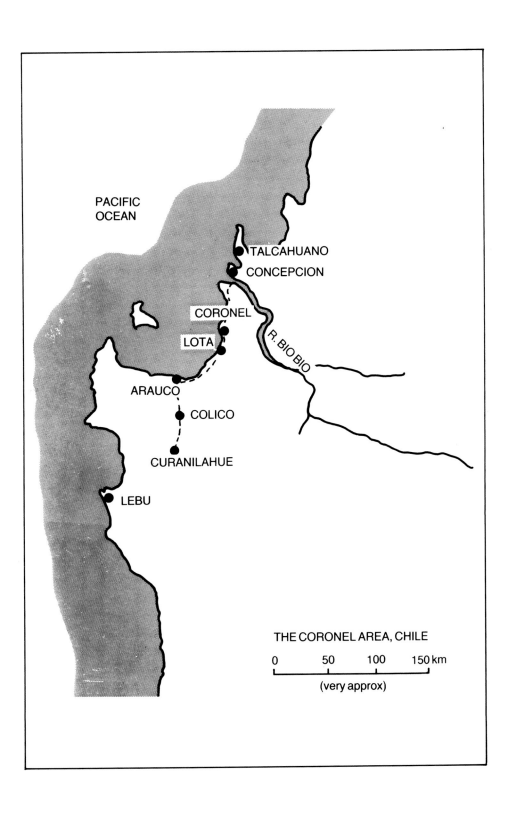

PACIFIC
OCEAN

TALCAHUANO

CONCEPCION

CORONEL

LOTA

R. BIO BIO

ARAUCO

COLICO

CURANILAHUE

LEBU

THE CORONEL AREA, CHILE

0   50   100   150 km

(very approx)

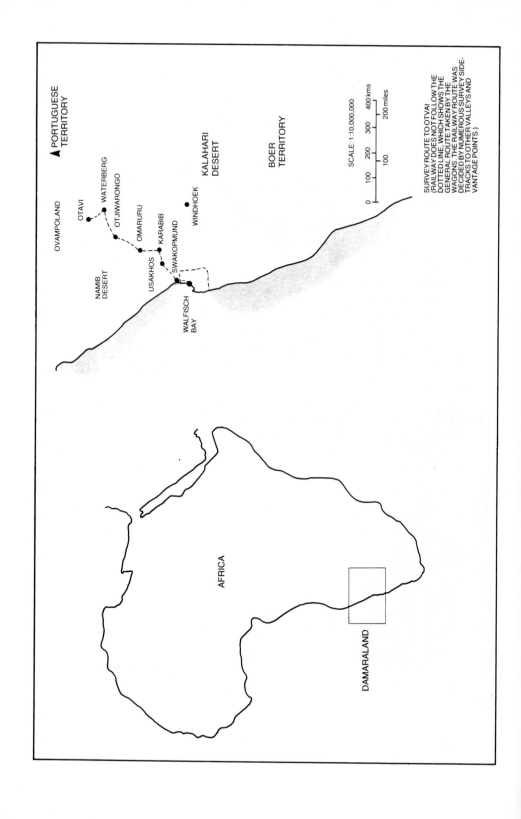

PORTUGUESE TERRITORY

OVAMPOLAND

OTAVI

WATERBERG

OTJIWARONGO

OMARURU

NAMIB DESERT

USAKHOS

KARABIB

SWAKOPMUND

WINDHOEK

WALFISCH BAY

KALAHARI DESERT

BOER TERRITORY

SCALE: 1:10,000,000

0   100   200   300   400 kms

100   200 miles

SURVEY ROUTE TO OTVAI
(RAILWAY DOES NOT FOLLOW THE
DOTTED LINE, WHICH SHOWS THE
GENERAL ROUTE TAKEN BY THE
WAGONS. THE RAILWAY ROUTE WAS
DECIDED BY NUMEROUS SURVEY SIDE-
TRACKS TO OTHER VALLEYS AND
VANTAGE POINTS.)

AFRICA

DAMARALAND

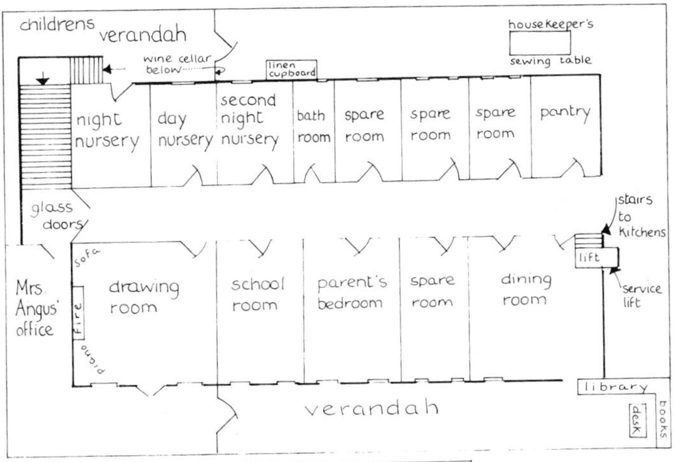

The Angus house at Coronel

Floor plan labels (upper plan):
- childrens verandah
- house keeper's sewing table
- wine cellar below
- linen cupboard
- night nursery
- day nursery
- second night nursery
- bath room
- spare room
- spare room
- spare room
- pantry
- glass doors
- stairs to Kitchens
- lift
- sofa
- Mrs Angus' office
- drawing room
- school room
- parent's bedroom
- spare room
- dining room
- service lift
- picture, fire
- library, desk, books
- verandah

The Angus house at Coronel

The large flat above the station and company administration offices. The flat was entirely surrounded by a large glassed-in verandah. The Kitchens and staff bedrooms were on the ground floor.

Drawn by Lynda Walton from a drawing by Louie Angus (Mrs. A.I.L. Proctor, Somerset)

The Angus house at Colico

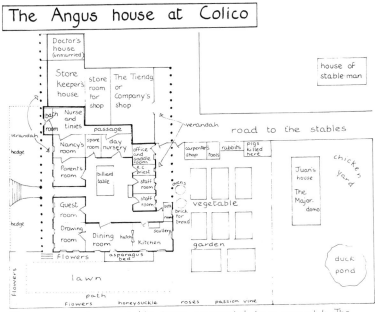

Floor plan labels (lower plan):
- railway
- Doctor's house (unmarried)
- Store Keeper's house
- store room for shop
- The Tienda or Company's shop
- house of stable-man
- bath room
- Nurse and tinies
- passage
- verandah
- road to the stables
- hedge
- Nancy's room
- spare room
- day nursery
- office and saddle room
- R C priest
- carpenter's shop
- tools
- rabbits
- pigs killed here
- chicken yard
- Parents room
- billiard table
- staff room
- ovens
- Juan's house
- The Major-domo
- Guest room
- staff room
- path
- brick room for bread
- vegetable
- Drawing room
- Dining room
- hatch
- Kitchen
- scullery
- garden
- duck pond
- hedge
- flowers
- asparagus bed
- lawn
- flowers
- path
- flowers   honeysuckle   roses   passion vine

This was a wooden ranch-like house, surrounded by a verandah. The nursery bathroom was added after the death of Bell, aged 4 (see page   ). The central billiard room had a glass roof to give light. Drawn by Lynda Walton from a drawing by Mary-cita Angus (Mrs. W. Scott Stevenson of N.S.Wales, Australia.)

The Angus Family Tree

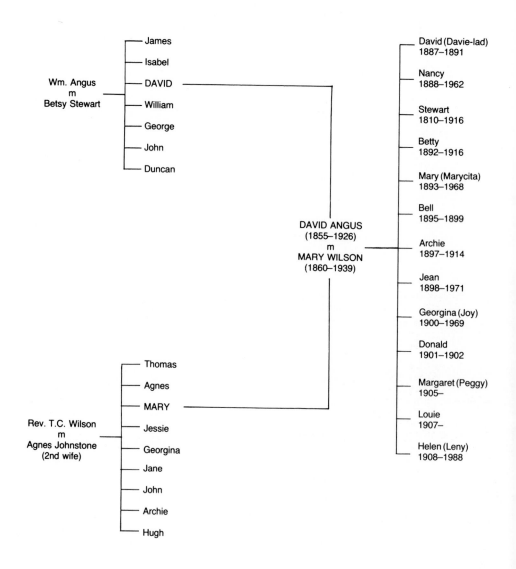

Wm. Angus
m
Betsy Stewart

- James
- Isabel
- DAVID
- William
- George
- John
- Duncan

DAVID ANGUS
(1855–1926)
m
MARY WILSON
(1860–1939)

Rev. T.C. Wilson
m
Agnes Johnstone
(2nd wife)

- Thomas
- Agnes
- MARY
- Jessie
- Georgina
- Jane
- John
- Archie
- Hugh

- David (Davie-lad) 1887–1891
- Nancy 1888–1962
- Stewart 1810–1916
- Betty 1892–1916
- Mary (Marycita) 1893–1968
- Bell 1895–1899
- Archie 1897–1914
- Jean 1898–1971
- Georgina (Joy) 1900–1969
- Donald 1901–1902
- Margaret (Peggy) 1905–
- Louie 1907–
- Helen (Leny) 1908–1988

Chapter Six

LIFE AND WORK IN URUGUAY 1887-1889

The midway point on David's Uruguayan railway survey was Paysandu, a small town on the River Uruguay some distance upstream from Fray Bentos and the River Plate. Here David rented rooms at the seedy Hotel Paris until a proper house could be found. He also engaged a maid for Mary and the baby, and a man servant called Albino to protect them during his absences on the survey. Then in September 1887 David and Mary vacated Mrs. Henderson's house (where they left many of their possessions in storage) and set off on a river paddleboat for Paysandu.

After a fortnight in the hotel David found a long, low white-painted house with two patios and a verandah. The walls of the inner patio were entirely covered with vines, but it turned out that the man servant Albino was a vineyard expert from Italy who, with his nephew Pedro, had come to South America to earn enough money to pay off the mortgage on the family farm in Italy. Before long Pedro was added to the Angus servants and that summer the vines were a huge success. They had clothes baskets full of grapes the size of plums.

During their first six weeks in Uruguay, David was only home with Mary for two nights. Sometimes he was able to look in during the day if he was passing through the town, but mostly the company required him at work out in the country. David's letters to Mary always promised that he would see her in a day or two, but her hopes were invariably dashed each time they were raised. David was always an optimist – most letters would begin with an apology for not coming home as promised, yet again, but by the end of each letter he would be promising all over again to be back soon. At this point David and Mary had been married little over a year, and eventually even David's spirits began to sag as the strain of ever-lengthening separation grew. He rarely showed it, but in a scribbled P.S. to a letter the frustration is obvious: 'Oh! How I wish I were home again, my Darling – I am afraid Mr. Gale will want me to remain with them here until I get them across the Rio Salsepuedes though . . .'

This early period in the survey and construction of the line was certainly hectic. By now David had been made resident engineer for the contractors and he spent weeks constantly travelling by coach or horse up and down the proposed line with his counterpart Mr. Gardiner, the engineer for the railway company. One task was to settle the assistant engineers at intervals along the route in the *caselias,* temporary huts which held about six unmarried men. At first wives without children were allowed to stay with their husbands if they did not mind living in tents, but when David discovered that after a bad storm two ladies had monopolised a hut while the men had crowded into inadequate tents he insisted that all wives go to the nearest towns until their husbands could provide them with homes of their own near the line.

David often went surveying on horseback with native cowboys or vacqueros who knew the countryside, but even here there were many potential problems – the bad roads, streams swollen by thunderstorms into raging torrents, lame horses, marker poles wrongly positioned by others, and in David's case the discomfort of piles. Letters to Mary from remote corners also show how he sometimes depended on the generosity of local farmers: '. . . an estancia with a Brazilian family named Meyrelles, where we stayed all night. They were very kind and made dinner for us after we arrived about 9 at night, and very dark.'

Life was also very busy for Mary. The Angus house had grown into a kind of hostel for company employees passing through Paysandu. Some company officials made it their home for weeks at a time, but there were also engineers in transit, the wives of others, and many more ex-patriates just looking for European company. Of course there were never enough beds for these people, but David had hooks fitted along the walls of the living room and kitchen and hammocks were slung across these rooms each evening. Male guests soon got used to this arrangement, for it was the same at every house along the trail.

At this point the maid left at an hour's notice but Mary found a little girl to help her in the kitchen and another to wash the baby. Even with Pedro and Albino as well she was still extremely busy cooking and making some sort of accommodation for all the visitors. She described this in a letter to her mother:

'. . . It is rather difficult arranging for them all when we have so little furniture. Yesterday we got a room ready for Mr. Gardiner by changing the furniture round in our room and using packing cases. We have only one small basin-stand in the house and no dressing tables, but I am covering some packing cases with brightly covered pink frills and putting toilet covers or towels on top. The house will look very nice when finished. We bought a big second-hand iron bed-stead with a straw mattress for ourselves, even that cost £5, we also got two second-hand single iron beds and a camp bed, so that we now have four beds in the house. The old man who looks after the garden varnished the two sitting room floors and we have strips of matting in the centre. My sewing machine is a great help in making draperies to cover the packing cases. I am going to make a couch of the big coffin (a large chest), putting stuffing and ticking on top and then covering it all with chintz. I must make myself one or two plain print dresses for the house as we have such a dirty kitchen, you can't keep it clean. The floor is like Cathedral Street in Dunkeld in the old days, only the holes between the stones are much deeper and when it rains the house is simply swimming – but for all that it is very *nice* house and plenty of room.'

It was natural that Europeans in South America tended to form communities, and most would travel well out of their way to visit others whenever possible. Despite the strain on housekeeping, Mary actually enjoyed this busy contact with other English-speaking people. Quite a few were Scottish and were able to bring news of her family, or take gifts back to Edinburgh for her. In the evenings any guests would sit with the Anguses on the patio with the sitting room door open, listening to someone playing their rented piano, the men perhaps enjoying a smoke and a yarn. There was no church yet in Paysandu, but an Episcopalian minister occasionally came upriver from Fray Bentos to give a service. On most other Sundays people gathered round the Angus piano for hymn singing.

One problem about living almost as pioneers in a developing country was the lack of medical care. Most people had to deal with illnesses as best they could with whatever common-sense knowledge they had. David was usually very fit and healthy but Mary suffered throughout her life from migraine. It seems to have been pretty severe, as this extract describes:

'I have not been very well lately with sick headaches, fearfully sick . . . the last three Sundays I have had attacks when I could scarcely open my eyes.'

In summer Mary also suffered from prickly heat, but the standard Victorian remedy for this was Eno's Fruit Salts sent out from Britain.

More serious were the illnesses which could claim little children. There was an English doctor, a Dr. French, in Paysandu but as David wrote to his parents: 'I don't think he knows much about babies and we have no English-woman who has an experience to advise us . . .' Even David, for all his down-to-earth attitudes to people, was so much the product of Victorian Britain that he hesitated to seek the knowledge of mere local natives. Meanwhile Davie-lad fell ill with whooping cough and then dysentry, from which his parents feared he might even die. Eventually he recovered, but these were worrying days for the Anguses.

At Christmas time (high summer in Uruguay) David and Mary attended a party at the house of Dr. French. He was a bachelor but 'local' English wives (from estancias up to even 30 miles away) rallied round to provide the tea and entertainments. In the evening on the patio they all watched charades acted by the doctor's staff, by the light of Japanese lanterns hung from trailing vines. Davie-lad was still very ill but when David went to check he was well and the Anguses enjoyed the party until two in the morning – a very different Christmas from the family back home.

Soon after this Dr. French was appointed doctor to the railway company and gave up his practice at Paysandu. David described the new arrangement in a letter: 'Everyone at work on the line from the peones to the engineers have to pay the doctor 50 cents a month, whether they are ill or well, and he undertakes to attend them and to supply all medicines free. As there will be an enormous number of workmen I suppose he will make a very good thing out of it. Perhaps he won't give quite so many medicines when he has to pay for them himself.' Despite David's cynicism it was a helpful and far-sighted improvement in workers' conditions at the time.

By now the survey work on the line was well advanced. David's work covered much more than simply marking out the route with posts. For example, he designed and supervised the construction of a jetty at Paysandu where materials and rolling stock could be unloaded from ships. He was also involved in obtaining land for the railway, as in this typical diary note: 'The owners of this *pulperia* also own all the camps (open land) hereabouts and will give land gratis if the line is brought past here.' Jottings in field notebooks illustrate the variety of other duties, ranging from 'rules for dealing with contractors' prices over wagons' or 'barrel drains and arch culverts' to 'general rules for calculating roughly the cubic contents in masonry of any culvert, open or closed, in railway or other embankments of any width or slope'. Notes also refer to the passes required for workmen, the erection of the telegraph system along the railway route, and so on.

By now more senior engineers were arriving from England to take overall charge of the construction work. Having completed the definitive survey from Paso de Los Toros, through Paysandu to the northern town of Salto, David was now given the Paso de los Toros-Paysandu section to construct – a distance of over 200 kilometres with all its bridges, cuttings and other problems. Soon David realised that the company wanted his house at Paysandu for their officials and once again he had to find somewhere to live – poor Mary dreaded the thought of yet another flitting, little realising how many more she would have to make over the years. 'I don't know how we are ever going to get packed up,' she wrote to her mother. 'The day's routine seems to take up all my time as it is, but I suppose we will warstle through.' By now Mary was also expecting her second baby.

Eventually David found a wooden house high on the open camp half way along his stretch of line. It was about three miles from an estancia or ranch called Los Merinos owned by an Englishman called Bridger. David called his house 'The Braes'.

In a letter to her mother Mary described the journey to this new home:

'We started last Wednesday from Paysandu in the office coach with two drivers and four horses. We had two days' journey, but a very pleasant one on the whole. We stopped at all the little wooden houses on the way. At the first one we had beautiful coffee and bread and butter, the butter home-made by means of an ordinary egg-beater – this was at about 10.00 o'clock. We changed horses there and went on to the Costabadies' house where we had 11.00 o'clock breakfast and changed horses again. We got to the Watsons' house a little before 4.00 o'clock in time for afternoon tea. The country all along was very pretty undulating leagues of camp with little houses and a few trees every few miles. It got dark very quickly after we left the Watsons and the driver was afraid we would not be able to reach the Craufords' house for the night, so we stopped at a Brazilian's estancia, thinking we could sleep there. However this Brazilian did not welcome us very cordially, so there was nothing for it but to push on the other two leagues to the Craufords'. For the last two miles it was quite dark, no road and several cuttings in the stream to cross and we were a long time finding one crossing, and we were very glad indeed to see the lights from their house in the distance. The house is in the middle of a plantation of palm trees and looks very picturesque . . . We had a comfortable night there and started again the next morning with David and Mr. Crauford doing work at intervals along the line as we went . . . Our own house looks very well but is rather coldly situated on high ground in the open camp without any trees or bushes of any kind. As the carpenters were still at work we drove on to the estancia, getting there about 5.00 p.m. The Bridgers are all away but the servants made us comfortable and we stayed till Monday . . . When we came away they gave us some bread and vegetables to start housekeeping with. Already in three days we have eaten a sheep and a leg of beef! This new cook of ours is used to camp ways, which entail throwing away a great deal of meat. She was highly recommended by the doctor but is very native in some of her ways too . . .'

It must have been very difficult to settle in to The Braes knowing that when work on the line was completed they might have to move again. By now winter was creeping in and by June the weather was so cold that the Anguses had to keep a roaring fire going in the stove. Although Mary was expecting her second baby, she was meanwhile kept busy enough by Davie-lad, as father dryly noted: 'Mary and the young man are quite well but he does not sleep much at night, so neither do we.'

The Braes may have been isolated but it was still a very bustling place. Not only was there a drawing office for David's charts and plans, but there were also two extra bedrooms fitted with bunks for the endless stream of visitors. Every house along the line offered hospitality as a matter of course for anyone passing through, and many young men chilled by winter on the camp found warmth around the Angus stove.

David also found that many of the local farmers were of Scottish descent, as he described to his parents: 'The local member of Congress is Eduard McEachen, the son of a Scotsman and as Scotch as possible. There is a family about 50 miles from here called MacKinnon, the father married the local heiress, hence the land, large tracts of it. Further up the river there are Leightons, Campbells, Drysdales, Stirlings etc. etc. and all very Scottish still, yet we are the only Scotch people on the staff.'

By September the birth of Mary's baby was approaching. David wanted her to go back to Paysandu for the birth, but Mary argued that if their neighbour Mrs. Bridger had managed to have her numerous children out there, then she could do the same. Unlike the Anguses, however, the Bridgers had three English women servants and a governess, so in the end David engaged a midwife or *matrona* to come out by diligence when the baby was due. This midwife actually arrived several weeks too soon ('I would oblige her if I could,' wrote Mary, 'especially as the pay coach from the office will be here with lots of people, and I would rather be out of sight when they are here'). By the time the baby, a healthy girl whom they called Nancy, was born on October 7th, 1888, the midwife was needed at her own house where one of her daughters was also expecting a baby. To make matters worse, the day before the birth David and the doctor were called to an accident on the line 100 leagues away, where several men had been badly hurt. Almost as soon as they had ridden off, Mary's pains began and her labour lasted from Friday to Sunday. All the time the matrona was in a fever to be off, and just two days after the birth she told Mary that she must go when the diligence passed, but that she would send someone else to take her place. So Mary simply had to sit up in bed and look after the baby herself. The only servants were Pedro and Albino, but Mary sent Pedro off to the estancia and Mrs. Bridger sent one of her daughters over to be with Mary. On the next diligence the matrona's replacement arrived – her mother! – a negress of about 70 with snow-white fuzzy hair. When she discovered that Pedro and Albino were the only servants she sent for one of her own grandsons as a chaperone for herself – Mary and the Bridger girl were not considered adequate. In those days a new mother was supposed to lie still for the first week or two after the birth, but having to sit up at once and get up sooner than she would normally have done did Mary no harm – indeed this would be the correct treatment today. Mary always said that she got over this birth more easily and more quickly than any of her other twelve.

Although the nearby Bridger family were busy with sheep shearing, their children rode over constantly to see that Mary was all right, especially when David was away. At this point the Bridgers were looking for a new governess and Mary began to build castles in the air about getting one of her sisters to come out to this post, or perhaps as a teacher. If they did not find employment, they would certainly find husbands in that woman-starved outpost, though this was only hinted at delicately in letters home. In fact the post of governess was soon filled by a young lady rejoicing in the name of Miss Birdie Ralph (and who very soon became engaged, just as Mary had expected). Unknown to Mary, at this moment her mother was ill and her sisters were reluctant to leave her bedside, but later Jessie did come out to South America, where she married. Meanwhile brother Tom was already working in Buenos Aires. David had tried unsuccessfully to have him appointed assistant accountant to the railway, but eventually Tom found a bookkeeper's job at about £300 a year in Buenos Aires. David also urged his own younger brothers to come out, and soon John Angus arrived at Buenos Aires where he was met by David who found him a job at Paysandu. Later still brother George also came out for a short time before moving on to a successful life elsewhere in South America. At first David tried to arrange jobs for these various relations, but this caused more trouble than it was worth and he soon gave up. In such a land of opportunity, only incompetent or lazy wasters would fail to do well, he reasoned, and then they would not have been worth helping anyway.

In the Uruguyan outback distances mattered little. People travelled miles just to visit other English settlers in their estancias. Most men went about on horseback but ladies quite often travelled by diligence or coach. In South America at this time these were often drawn by ten horses, spread out in two groups of five like the fingers on a hand. An outrider on an eleventh horse went ahead to check the road surface and keep a look-out for bandits. This outrider was called the *quartiador,* or sometimes the *conquistador,* and he often had a twist in his neck and a wry face from constantly turning round to see if the coach was still following across the open camp. Sometimes there was only the faintest trail to follow, and because of the great summer heat diligences often travelled at night.

One day David and Mary were travelling across the camp in just such a coach, with the horses straining at their traces and the quartiador riding ahead, when shots were suddenly fired from low hills nearby. A crowd of men rode up, firing shots in the air and shouting for the driver to stop. The horses were pulled up with some difficulty and a tremendous jolt. When the bandits had encircled the coach they made all the passengers alight. Mary had the new baby in her arms while their little maid Antonia clutched Davie-lad. The men were told to put their hands above their heads while the bandits removed their purses, watches, guns and anything else of value they could see. While this was going on, another man rode up. Like the others he had a handkerchief tied across the lower part of his face, but he seemed to be the leader. Despite the mask, David thought he recognised him and called his name. Immediately the situation changed – the handkerchief was pulled down and the man shook David by the hand, calling him his dear Senor Angus, his honoured friend Don David and using all sorts of complimentary expressions. The bandits were ordered to return all the valuables (which they did with very bad grace and surly looks), the passengers were ushered back into the coach and off they went again, only this time with an escort of bandits who rode around the coach in great circles shooting their guns in the air!

David explained that the bandit leader had been Minister of the Interior in the last government, but having lost the last election and failed in the inevitable revolution, he was filling in time as a bandit leader until the next revolution. David knew him from earlier railway negotiations with the government, while presumably the bandit leader thought it prudent to keep in with the English railway people, in case he ever became Minister of the Interior again.

By mid-1888 David's section of railway was nearing completion and the question of his next employment began to matter. Victorian Scotland was full of worthies who had been village schoolmasters or local doctors in the same place for years and years, but for an engineer the completion of every project renewed worries of unemployment and destitution. A competent man in South America would probably find something, but it was still an anxious time until he did. All through his work in Uruguay, David had kept several other irons in the fire for just this moment, as in this letter reference: 'I am glad Morrow and Glasgow went to San Nicolas about that survey. I don't want Bengolea to think I'm neglecting either of his schemes.' David seems mostly to have assumed that he would find work in Argentina, for in another letter he wrote: 'Mr. Ward was here yesterday about the construction to Tucuman on the Rosario Railway . . . and it is possible I might have an offer for them.' In fact there was an offer. By now David's brother George was working for the Buenos Aires and Rosario Railway Company and may have let them know of David's position, for the manager T. C. Clarke offered him joint construction of the Tucuman extension with another engineer called Tetley but starting when work actually began, which would be some time yet. David even signed a contract, for here at least was a positive opportunity, albeit in the future.

Meanwhile the Uruguayan railway was nearly complete and David's employers Perry Cutbill de Lunga were also looking around for more construction opportunities, especially in

Buenos Aires. Unfortunately this period in the late 1880's was a time of revolution and upheaval in Argentina and little construction was under way – officials and governments could not be sure of staying in power for long. Permission for construction schemes was so often delayed or countermanded that railway building became neglected for a time. Foreign companies and investors did not know who to deal with and so held back for the moment. There were several concessions available however – proposed routes which earlier governments had already agreed to – and for the moment most companies simply investigated the feasability of these schemes, pin-pointing suitable routes and making plans for the day when applications to construct could be put forward to a more settled administration. Surveyors were busy, even if the constructors were not. As a result some routes were found to be not viable; a line from Nueve de Julis to San Rafael was abandoned, for example, because of the problems of crossing a vast salt desert. It was at this time of surveying for the future that David hoped to find work in Argentina.

In October 1888 David was sent by his company to Buenos Aires, and from there inland to make a flying survey of the Cordoba and North Western route. This produced a favourable report and while it was being considered David spent the time making a detailed survey of the proposed line from Mendoza to San Rafael. This was the small town close to Monte Cuman, where David had surveyed in early 1887. At that time he had foreseen the need for a railway by making an unofficial preliminary survey of a possible route – the very same route which he was now re-examining more thoroughly.

When this survey was also completed, David was asked to make detailed estimates and costs for the Cordoba and North Western line, with the probability that he would be put in charge of the eventual construction work. Clearly the future once more lay in Argentina, so in January 1889 Mary packed all their belongings and rather sadly left The Braes for a hotel in Paysandu. Meanwhile David looked for a house around Cordoba, where he expected to be working soon. For a time he lived at Mrs. Henderson's house in Buenos Aires, using the time between consultations with his employers and meetings with officials to polish up the estimates he had made for the Cordoba railway. Night after night he went over his figures and calculations, trying to bring them down to a competitive price. One typical problem was the question of the earth-works, which were too expensive – his line involved too many costly cuttings and embankments, and he had to revise his plans to reduce this.

Eventually the company decided to go ahead with the Cordoba and North Western line and David was asked to collect a workforce and obtain materials for the work. As a result of this firm offer, David withdrew from the contract he had made for the Tucuman extension, and concentrated his energies on the Cordoba project. A letter from February 1889 illustrates the arrangements he was making:

'Dear Sir,
It being probable that we shall have to transport about 10,000 tons of railway plant and material to Cordoba this year, could you kindly furnish a quotation for freight from Rosario to Cordoba for such a quantity, including discharging from vessels and loading into wagons, if you can arrange it.
Yours truly,
per Perry, Cutbill de Lungo and Co.
(signed) David Angus.

It soon became clear that formidable difficulties stood in the way of this project, most seriously the hindrance of official red tape at the Cordoba provincial government. The provincial governor was a brother of the Argentinian president and had to be treated with great care and respect by David, while all the time he fretted at the delays and difficulties which resulted. David always preferred active work to the tedium of negotiations and meetings.

And there were other difficulties. Living costs were much higher than they had been in Uruguay, and David wondered if Mary and the children would be as well off as before. Skilled workmen were difficult to obtain and some let him down by deserting. It was not easy to find a suitable house. The work would also require him to be away from home a lot, and he had promised Mary that he would see more of her in future.

By now the hotel at Paysandu was becoming expensive and there was pressure on David to seal a definite appointment from his company for the actual construction work. Flying surveys and preliminary work required for a railway scheme were often made for no payment by engineers in the hope that they would be put in charge of the later construction work. This was the case with David, but still nothing had been settled about the future, while letters like this one from Mary emphasised their increasing financial difficulties:

'I have just counted up my money and find I have 35 dollars and 55 cents. I went out and bought some toys for Davie as he had nothing to play with. For 1 dollar 50 cents I brought home – a wooden horse, a tin coach with two horses, an India rubber squeaky doll for Nancy, a mechanical humming top and three coloured glass balls. Davie has broken them a little but he is so happy with them. I have paid for the baby's cradle and mattress but not for the bath yet, nor the 9 dollars 20 cents we spent the other day on gloves, stockings etc. and I still have the dressmaker and washing to pay for, so I won't have much if anything over after paying Antonia (their girl servant) and Pedro at the end of the month . . . I wish you were here . . . I cannot feel right when you are away. I do hope we will get settled soon so that you need not be so much away.'

In March 1889 David sent for Mary and the children to come to Buenos Aires, and once again they had to pack up and move. The little maid Antonia, who was learning reading and writing from Mary, decided to come too, and so did Pedro and Albino. The Anguses lived with Mrs. Henderson, who again unfailingly offered accommodation when it was needed. The servants lived somewhere else but turned up at Mrs. Henderson's guesthouse every morning to help out. Meanwhile David continued making arrangements for the Cordoba railway scheme.

Then quite suddenly matters came to a head. The company put an older engineer in charge of the Cordoba construction and instead, out of the blue, they offered David full charge of another scheme in Paraguay. It sounds as though he was 'bought off' to make way for a more senior man, but David's enthusiasm for the Cordoba work was dropping anyway, and this offer was too good to refuse. The contract shows that David was to receive £2,000 per year, plus a bonus of 5 per cent on all net profits made by the railway he was to build. He would also have removal expenses from Buenos Aires to Paraguay, and later home to Britain at the end of the work. They would also provide him with a 'reasonable and proper dwelling house' and pay all reasonable travelling and other expenses incurred by him in Paraguay or elsewhere for the purposes of his work. In short, this was definitely promotion.

Of course there was a snag. Paraguay was still a little known land, from which came very conflicting stories and descriptions. For years the country had been decimated by terrible wars – during the Lopez revolutions of 1865-70 the population had fallen from about 1 million to 221,000 and three-quarters of all the country's males were killed. Lopez was still remembered as a tyrant and revolutions still flared up from time to time, so would this be a safe place to raise a family? Stories also described the unhealthy swamps of Paraguay and the lack of doctors. In fact roads, postal services, hotels, sewage and water services, telegraph links, even schools and industries hardly existed in a country yet to be developed. On the other hand there were optimists who saw Paraguay as a paradise, a new land of promise and opportunity where hardworking people could settle and make a future. There was land and water and sun – all that was needed for people of spirit and vision to develop the country and make it flourish.

With the Anguses there was little doubt about the decision. David sided with the optimists and agreed to go. In just two hectic weeks he assembled a workforce and the necessary stores for Paraguay. Then in March 1889 David, Mary and their two infants boarded a river paddle-boat for the 1,000 kilometre voyage up the River Parana to Asuncion, the Paraguayan capital city. This time it was very much a journey into the unknown.

Chapter Seven

UPS AND DOWNS IN PARAGUAY 1889-1891

In March 1889 the Anguses set off for Paraguay – David, Mary, the two infants, the men servants Pedro and Albino, the maid Antonia, and a few company officials including the accountant, a Mr. Duff from Pitlochry in Scotland. For six days they travelled 1,000 kilometres up the River Parana by Mississippi-type paddleboat to Asuncion, the capital city – indeed the only city in that country of less than one million people.

It seems that one of those frequent South American revolutions was in progress during the voyage, for the boat made unofficial stops every night at make-shift landing places. Here there were whispered confabulations as shadowy men got off and others got on. The vessel was also boarded several times by police or soldiers but no rebels or suspects were ever found. Meanwhile the passengers had to exist as best they could for there were few comforts. Fortunately the boat carried goats for milk and live chickens which amused the children and fed them all, although Mary never actually used the goats' milk. She always travelled with crates of Nestles milk for safety.

At that time Paraguay was an almost unknown country to people in Europe. As one of the smaller South American republics, it was divided into two differing parts by the River Paraguay. To the west lay the wild country of the Grand Chaco, a vast region of forests, swamps and grass lands lying mostly within the tropics and inhabited by Indians. In 1889 only the fringe of this area was known and the primitive state of the natives was only just being described in books by the Rev. W. Barbrooke Grubb (who worked for the South American Missionary Society and has been called the 'Livingstone of South America'). While the eastern and southern parts of Paraguay were certainly less primitive than the Chaco, to a European they would also have been very wild. Little had been done yet to develop the land, roads were still dirt tracks, farms were just subsistence small-holdings and most Western ideas of 'civilisation' were unknown beyond the capital city.

David's job was to construct a railway from Asuncion eastwards through this more fertile area and then south to the

River Parana where northern Argentina began. An older railway already ran about sixty miles eastwards from Asuncion; David was to improve this line and then complete the route southwards. He decided to make his headquarters at Villa Rica, a dilapidated small town halfway along the route, from where he would be able to travel in either direction to supervise the survey and construction work. He set off for Villa Rica as soon as all official business had been completed in Asuncion, leaving Pedro and Albino to follow in a bullock cart loaded with furniture and baggage. Mary, Antonia and the children stayed behind at a seedy Italian hotel – it was the bullfighting season and crowds were in town, making it impossible to obtain rooms, so they stayed in the annexe of a gambling and drinking saloon.

David's three day journey quickly showed what he would be up against when he got down to work. At first he travelled on the existing rickety railway but the engine did not fit the gauge and three times it came off the rails. When he eventually reached the end of the line he continued on horseback but the ground was water-logged from heavy rain and many roads were impassable. David soon realised that if the railway was typical of local efficiency or the rain of the local climate, he would have many problems to face.

The first priority at Villa Rica was to obtain a house, but on the first day David found nothing. Then he met Dr. Bottrel, who had come with his wife from England to find a cure for tuberculosis in the reputedly beneficial Paraguayan climate.* Dr. Bottrell soon found David a house – a typical mud-brick adobe dwelling which David later described as 'nae sae verra hielant!', but which he nevertheless rented for six months. Next day Pedro and Albino arrived and David left them to get the house in some sort of order while he went back for Mary and the children.

Mary was particularly relieved when David returned, for she had been very anxious about Antonia, whose head had been turned by the handsome bullfighters in town. Some were living in the same hotel and she had now plastered yards and yards of cheap lace all over her dress to make herself 'look sharp'. Just in time, it seemed, David has returned to lead them to Villa Rica.

---

*Dr. Bottrell lived to a good old age and had a family. Descendants still live in Paraguay.

There was more official business to complete first, so while David met government officials, Mary had a chance to see something of the city. It was mostly an old Spanish mission town but one attraction was that the streets were all lined with orange trees. It was said that the only good thing ever done by the tyrant Lopez was to order everyone to plant orange trees – oranges even became an export for a time – and now as Mary went around in a horse-drawn tram car she could reach out from the upper deck and pick the fruit as it was in season.

Eventually the Anguses set out for Villa Rica. With them went a few company people including a bridge builder called Herd and a carpenter called McAndrew. Mary later described their eventful journey in a letter-cum-journal which so fascinated the families at home that it was passed around the Anguses and Wilsons. It is given here almost in full:

'We arrived here all safe and sound on Tuesday night, 30th April, after a long and highly exciting journey from Asuncion, which we had left nearly a week before. It seems that Tuesday is a very unlucky day in this country on which to begin a journey or to begin a new business, and so it proved for us. On the previous night we had told the hotel people, 'On waking call us early' as our train started at 6.00 a.m. They did not waken, leastwise they did not call us early enough, consequently we arrived at the station just in time to see the last carriage of our train leave the platform. We were very philosophic about it, considering we had bundled the children into their clothes and into a tram in the middle of torrents of rain at 5.30 a.m. in the morning! We had a good cup of coffee in the station, grumbling all the time at the tramway driver for being so slow and the train for being so quick. Then we just took the first tram back to our deserted rooms at the Cancha to find them already stripped of all signs of our habitation. There was only one train a day to the end of the line, but we found that a train went out about twenty miles, leaving Asuncion at 3.00 p.m. so we took this train thinking it better to sleep the night at Arequa station than risk missing the train again at 6.00 a.m. We should have reached our destination for the night in less than 2 hours but the line was in such a bad state it simply crawled, stopping at every station and the jolts were worse than a diligence by a long way. At each station there were women selling *chipa*, a kind of native bread made from mandioca and also fruit. We bought bread, bananas and two ready cooked fowls at one station and it was as well that we had a meal on the train as we did not get to Arequa till between nine and ten at night and all we would get there was tinned salmon and a very little black bread and black coffee. We had a comfortable night upstairs in the station *fonda*, in little rooms partitioned half-way up to the roof with corrugated iron. It was much pleasanter not having to get up so early next morning to catch the through train . . .

Next day, Wednesday 1st May, we got aboard the train at about 8.00 a.m. and went creeping along as before, till beginning to gain a little more confidence the driver quickened up a little and then came jolt after jolt in quick succession and the train was off the rails! I must say I got a good fright as the shock was severe. Our carriage was one of the ones off the rails with others both in front and behind. The train came to a stand-still of course and after about an hour and a half they managed to get some trucks back on the line and all we passengers got hoisted up into a goods wagon, then on we went arriving at Caballero station between 2 and 3 in the afternoon . . .

We hoped to be able to hire bullock carts at once at Caballero and continue our journey the same day, but no bullocks or carts were forthcoming and it was raining steadily so we had to make ourselves as comfortable as circumstances would permit in the *bolichi* or tavern. The accommodation consisted of two rooms with *catares* or camp beds, one room for the men and the other for our family. Our room was also the harness room for the whole establishment and while we were in bed a hen hatched out a brood of chickens close by my bed. Washing basin there was none, but as we had the baby's bath we were quite well off. The beds and sheets were simply horrible, we carefully took all the bedclothes off and put our own shawls etc. over them and even then we could hardly sleep for thinking of things creeping. We were there two nights amidst torrents of rain and a man began battering at our window and calling out, "Mr. Engineer let me in or I'll shoot you!" When David refused to let him in and told him to go away, he continued his battering and threatened to kill us all in five minutes if he did not get in. I was very frightened and got up with the baby ready to run and Antonia with Davie. David threatened to shoot him if he did not go away, and eventually he went off. We saw this man next day, he was quite mad and had a brick hidden in his shirt to throw at someone.

The rain went on for two days but on Friday afternoon David managed to secure two good bullock carts and we set out at once on our travels. Our baggage was placed as evenly as possible in the bottom of the carts and over this we placed mattresses to sit on, and so we started with Antonia and the children and me at the back of the first cart with David and the driver up in front. The rest were in the other cart. The motion was not unpleasant and when we got accustomed to the squeaking and groaning of the wooden axles, we enjoyed our trip very well.

We had hoped to get to a place called Ibitime that night, but we were utterly at the mercy of our driver and we had hardly gone half a league when he informed us that it was too late to go any further as this was the only place where we could buy meat for the rest of the journey . . . There was no help for it, so we set to work to get the carts ready to sleep in while the men got meat and cooked *asade* for us all. The rancho was covered with children and old women not one of whom spoke a word of Spanish. They swarmed round us and touched our clothes and seemed greatly impressed by the babies. They offered us their house to sleep in, but we declined after our last experiences we preferred our cart. This we arranged with bunks made from the mattresses we had with us. Antonia, Nancy and I on one side with David and wee Davie on the other. The next two nights we slept tolerably well but the first night David was restless and the pigs came grunting round the carts.

About 3.00 a.m. the cart men began to stir again, and made their maté (a kind of tea made from a species of holly), yoked the oxen and before 4.00 we were away again with the sun rising slowly beyond us. We crossed one or two very bad river passes and then got into a beautiful piece of meadow land with wooden hills at each side and the mountains in the distance. We stopped about 8.00 a.m. to pasture the bullocks and make tea for ourselves and we had a very nice picnic with sardines and a tin of tongue and biscuits. After a two hour stop we went on again, and had to pass a swamp over a mile long, where the bullocks were wading over their knees in water and the driver told us stories of the tremendous boa-constrictors which lived there, over 23 feet long which eat bullocks! We were glad to get to the end of that swamp and immediately after we left it we came to a wood full of oranges. I left the children with Antonia for a while and walked alongside David. Mr. McAndrew is an enthusiastic naturalist and was racing about with his butterfly net catching specimens.

About mid-day we got to the small town of Ibitime where we stopped again and had *desayuno* or breakfast. The inn was kept by a little Austrian with a tremendous wife. As soon as she saw us she pounced upon our dresses, especially Antonia's which she thought was very smart with all its lace. Could I cut her out a pattern to make one like it for her daughter, the fat wife asked, for the dressmaker in the town could not cut fashionable modes. So we set to work and cut a paper shape with a yoked body for the little girl to the intense delight of the father, who went off to his shop and brought back two pieces of print for me to cut out two dresses to the same pattern. The whole proceeding was very funny, but they were extremely serious over it, it seemed a matter of such importance to them! I must say I never thought of my clothes as being fashionable!

After breakfast we started again hoping to get to the house of a German before dark. However our cartman evidently did not wish to get there so he went slowly and shortly before 5.00 p.m. stopped right in the middle of an open camp and said he was not going any further that night . . . They arranged for fire and water and made soup and a roast, and we made tea and had another picnic and put the children to bed. They slept much better this time, and we sat up and talked by the light of the fire and a candle for a time, then went to bed as comfortably as we could.

On Sunday morning we started very early as before and came to a halt between 8.00 and 9.00 a.m. at a kind of village of huts on a wooded slope which stretched down to the river Tibicuari which we hoped to cross in canoes that day. We had soup and tea and tongue again and David and Mr. McAndrew and I sat under the cart with the children and sang some old hymns and paraphrases. It was a beautiful sunny morning and we thought our troubles were nearly over and we could get home to Villa Rica for certain the next day. What was our disgust when we arrived at the river about 4.00 p.m. to hear that we could not get across that night as the canoes were occupied with some carts coming from the other side and would not be finished before dusk. The mosquitoes were very bad too and it was very provoking as we had only come about two leagues altogether that day and if the cartman had only come on to the river without stopping for breakfast we could have crossed quite easily. We heard we could get comfortable beds in an inn on the other side, so leaving the carpenter and the peon in charge of the carts, the rest of us went over the river in a little canoe and spent the night at the inn.

The owner of the house greeted us most effusively when we arrived and escorted us to our rooms with a lordly air, expatiating all the way on the contents of his store and larder for all comers. "In this house," he said, "we want for nothing, hens, bacon, bread, tea, coffee, anything – ask exactly for what you want." We said we wanted dinner and after a time . . . he led us to the dining room and having arranged us all with all the airs of a master of ceremonies, he seated himself at the head of the table and acted as host. First we had soup, then an old woman brought in a piece of neck of beef and a thin old hen on one plate and some pumpkin on another. Our host made the hen go round the whole table which consisted of four French workmen besides our party, so there was not much for each. The beef was carried away again untouched but we lived in hopes of what was coming. Soon the old lady appeared again with a plate of plain boiled rice. The host shouted at her to ask the cook for the stew etc. but she said there was no stew in an indignant tone, as if telling him something already well known. The host then apologised for the want of the stew as if it were not his fault, and proceeded to serve the rice and that was the whole of the dinner. We suggested we would like some tea, and later on we had cups brought us, very weak and no milk. However, we had nice clean beds and slept well but for one excitement, poor wee Davie fell out of bed in the middle of the night with a fearful thump.

In the morning we had plenty of time to rest as news came across that our bullocks had strayed in the night and it might be hours before they were all across. So we made a raid on the man's stores and got sardines and *galletas* or camp biscuits to eat with our coffee and told our lordly host that we expected breakfast from him too. Some women came along selling live hens and eight chicks which we bought, basket and all. Then we let them out in our rooms and gave them maize and corn and had great fun getting them caught again before we started. The breakfast was as meagre as before and went round even less as two extra travellers turned up as well.

At last our bullocks and carts arrived across the river but it was 2.00 p.m. before we got started and we had no hope of reaching Villa Rica that night. In fact we did not go more than about a mile before our cartman announced that we were going to stop for the night. David was very angry with him (but of course they had had a long enough day catching the bullocks and swimming them across the river). At last the head man promised he would get us to Villa Rica the next day, Tuesday, for certain and we had to be content with that. It was a fearfully cold night and by 12.30 a.m. the men were so cold they could not sleep and got up and lit a fire and made maté. They started in the dark about 2.30 a.m. and by sunrise we had really come a long way. We stopped about 5.30 a.m. to feed the bullocks and make tea and then we went on through a long stretch of open camp, and about 10.00 o'clock stopped once more before entering the long cutting through a wood which lay between us and Villa Rica. We had been warned before that this road was very bad, and the cartman made all the men of the party walk all the way – but they had the best of it I can assure you. I wished many a time that I was walking too, when the cart was groaning along, one wheel on a level at least a yard higher than the other. I thought the babies would be pitched out, many a time, when we seemed to be on the edge of a precipice. At one place one of the bullocks stuck altogether in a hole and the one cart man dug at him with an iron pointed stick while the other whooped and yelled and raced round him. By sheer brute force they got the poor animal dragged out and on we went again, up more difficult passes than ever till we were within the last league of Villa Rica and our new home. Hope filled all our souls, when – crash! went our cart in a hole, our axle being completely smashed through, Nancy and I being thrown down in a corner of the cart with Antonia and Davie rolling on top of us! David and Mr. McAndrew, the carpenter, were away far ahead, chasing butterflies, but when they saw we had stopped they came back. We consulted what to do and made up our minds to walk on to the town with the children and enough things for the night and leave Mr. McAndrew in charge of the cart. Word had already been sent ahead to Albino to have dinner ready for us that night, and as it was a pleasant afternoon we quite enjoyed the walk except that the children were just a little too heavy to carry such a distance, though we took turns.

At last we came in sight of the town which is set in the most beautiful scenery we have yet seen. It is a wooded platform with slightly wooded slopes all round and in the distance grand mountains covered with thick forest. Were we not glad to get to our own house at last! David went on in front of us and disappeared round a corner. Shortly after, two figures appeared, running towards us. They did not look like Albino and Pedro but they did not look like natives either. One was a tall man and one was rather short with two black coat-tails wagging on each side as he ran. They were our two Scotch carpenters, Napier, the tall man and Davidson with the coat-tails flying . . . Then at the gate, there was Pedro all smiles and Albino came out of the kitchen, his big honest eyes speaking his pleasure at seeing us safe and sound. He had the house clean for us as hands could make it, and a nice rice pudding in the oven for Davie and dinner ready for the rest of us. I soon got sheets on our beds and a few things unpacked and we went to bed very thankful indeed to be in a home of our own once more.'

The new house was typical of the area, one storey high with a flat roof and built around a *saguan* or patio. There were no windows facing the street – all the rooms opened on to the patio for greater safety. Before long Mary was busy organising the household and unpacking – there was certainly plenty to do even without the babies and all the washing they entailed. Cooking, for example, was done in the open air on a long table of bricks arranged like a field kitchen, with two rows and iron bars across them heated by charcoal. There was also a beehive oven for bread. A whole faggot of wood was first burnt inside it, then the ashes were raked out and the bread dough was put into the oven on trays. Mary even made her own yeast, from a recipe in Warne's Cookery Book. By the time the oven had cooled the bread was properly baked.

In such a remote place Mary also had to make her own candles. She had first learned how to do this in Uruguay where the natives poured mutton fat into moulds, but the Paraguayan method was more laborious and messy. A great cauldron of boiling fat was suspended in the open air over a small bonfire, usually from the branch of a tree. Also hanging from the same branch was a flat metal plate with several cotton wicks hanging down. These wicks were repeatedly lowered into the burning fat, raised again to cool them, lowered again, and so on until a reasonably long candle had been made. As cooling was an essential part of the process it usually took place at night; Mary said that to see a group of old women crouched round a caudron with the firelight playing on their faces always reminded her of the witches in Macbeth.

For much of this time David was busy organising his workforce and he often had to leave Mary at Villa Rica. However there was at least the company of Dr. Bottrell and his wife, the only English residents in town. Mrs. Bottrell was just eighteen, and had been married only six months. She was already expecting a baby and Mary seems to have felt an immediate sympathy for the girl, stranded as she was by fortune in the wilds of Paraguay. As a prim lady from Eastbourne who thought she had married a normal doctor, only to find him immediately emigrating to South America for his health, it must all have come as something of a shock. 'It is not what she has been used to,' wrote Mary with a very Victorian observation.

Although they soon became friendly, Mary's first meeting with Mrs. Bottrell was especially memorable. Each year elections were held for half the deputies and senators in the Paraguayan government, but these were often bedevilled by sporadic minor revolutions as one side or the other refused to accept the results. On the Sunday after Mary's arrival an election was held in Villa Rica. Voting was held in the church, the only large building in the town and which stood in the centre of the market square or plaza. Most of the surrounding houses had flat roofs, however, and from them snipers shot at any voters they recognised as supporters of the other side. That day, within a week of coming to Villa Rica, Mary saw seven men shot dead as they crossed the plaza to vote. Dr. Bottrell was called out so often to help the wounded and dying that at the height of the trouble a young engineer called Bruce went to Mrs. Bottrell's house and brought the terrified young woman to the Angus house for greater safety. Here, sheltering from the bullets, the two ladies first met.

Next day David found several members of the losing party hiding on the roof of his house – quite probably they had been snipers themselves but now the problem was how to get them away safely. Over the next few days he managed to smuggle them out one at a time when workmen from the railway line called at the house. Nevertheless Mary was terrified of discovery and reprisals until the last man was safely gone.

A month later the Anguses moved to a bigger house and the first became an office for the company. This new house also had a patio, with a huge banana tree in the centre round which the dining table had been fixed. A snake changed its skin under this table one day when they were at dinner. Later David added a fireplace to the house, which resulted in the first chimney ever seen in Villa Rica, but it was still a very simple place. The floors were of rough brick, for example, and only one room had a ceiling instead of rafters. Mary also mentioned in a letter that 'there are only three houses in the whole town with glass in the windows and *ours* is not one of them.' The rooms were also very damp, which Victorians often blamed for childhood illnesses, but the place was at least home. In the end they lived there eighteen months.

By now David was also very busy on the railway line. In Brazil he had been one of the lesser engineers working on a particular stretch of work. In Argentina and Uruguay he had been in charge of longer sections with others working under him, but here in Paraguay he was fully in control – he had to appoint and supervise the lesser engineers and those in charge of longer sections. New responsibilities raised problems which David had not previously had to handle – liaising with the government's inspector, obtaining passes for his men, nego- tiating for land and keeping supplies, food, mail and pay moving so that no-one down the line would grumble. Every alteration to the line had to be approved by the government in Asuncion, but ministers there also changed a lot and most decisions had to be renegotiated several times as new people came to power. The whims of government officials also had to be accepted, and as a result the site for Villa Rica railway station, for example, was moved several times.

Even after the planning stage the sheer logistics of trying to build a railway in such a backward country presented new problems. Many of Parguay's trees were unfamilar to David and he had to discover which were suitable. Then a saw-mill was set up to provide railway sleepers and building timber but permission had to be obtained from Asuncion before a timber yard could be established beside the line. Later a brick works was also created and the production of the bricks for culverts and bridges began. Many supplies came up-river from Argentina or Uruguay, so when permission had to be obtained to use the wharf and cranes at Asuncion, David went straight to the President of Paraguay and received clearance to use these facilities free of charge – typical of the confident zest he always had for his work and how he could be at ease with presidents and peons alike.

One immediate problem was the shortage of male workers. So many men had died in the Lopez wars that now twenty years later women still greatly outnumbered men, some estimates say by as much as nine to one. As a result women did every kind of work in Paraguay – 'butchers, bakers and quite literally candlestick makers,' as Mary wrote in a letter. David refused to employ them on heavy railway work like tree-felling or digging, however, and in the end he had to send to colleagues in Argentina and Uruguay for extra labourers. When these men finally arrived David had to obtain passes and work permits for each of them at Asuncion.

Soon David was riding up and down the line getting his local engineers and their workers established. After surveying, the first job was to cut a rough *picada* or line through the undergrowth, but the route went through so many swamps and forests that David had to have gangs of men every two kilometres on some stretches. With the shortage of men David himself often helped to cut this picada, wading through swamps with his senior engineers for want of more peons. There were also scores of rivers often swollen by rain, but at this time not one had been bridged and everything had either to be ferried or swum across. Horses and bullocks were often lashed to canoes when crossing, but many drowned for want of a bridge. In the end David had the bridges built by his carpenters, though they had no connection with the actual railway line.

A look at David's diary illustrates the difficulties and rough life he was facing:

Saturday, 28th September, 1889: Young's men (employed digging cuttings) came and complained that they had been misled by him, that he had promised them $2 per day and that they could not make anything at 18 cents per cubic metre.

Wednesday, 2nd October: Started for surveyors' camp with Duff, Browning and Christophersen. Got as far as Don Ottoman's where we slept. Don O. is willing to give the land necessary for the line free if we put a station on his land. House at Dapilla Borja has been built on the skew, the municipality insisted on its being moved from the site I had chosen for it and put it in the corner of the street.

Thursday, 3rd October: Started early and rode to Sisto Ginienez's from whom we got a change of horses. Rained very heavily all morning. Rode as far as Bolicho Pepin, Kilometre 71. Slept in shed.

Friday, 4th October: Got to camp about 1.30 p.m. and had lunch. Went with Mr. Coakes and examined line of route to Rio Tebicuariguazu and the crossing of the Rio Pirapo. The river should be crossed by a span of 37.00 metres wide, on the other side are good building-stone outcrops which should be used for building piers and abutments.

Saturday, 5th October: Started from camp about 6.00 a.m. with Worsoe and Duff. Examined Ehrehart's line from Puesto Narangi to Kilometre 100, it would be quite as easily made as our own, but the land is very swamp and our line is on the hillside. Got to Sisto Gunienez's bolicho before dark.

Sunday, 6th October: Started at about 5.00 a.m., swam across the Herandaria – Yacuguazo still in flood. Home about 5.00 p.m. Went to ball at Claudio Gorostiagos.

Soon after most of the picada was finished and the work of levelling began. As with the line, gradients had to be kept to a minimum and surveyors worked hard to check that no section was too steep. In some places gangs of men dug cuttings with simple picks and shovels, sweating in the heat and wearing floppy hats to protect them from the sun. Elsewhere they heaped up embankments or erected wooden trestles across the swamps, and always David rode up and down the line giving instructions and encouragement, taking measurements or checking the rock beneath swamps and rivers.

Eventually Christmas came to Villa Rica. By then several more engineers and sub-contractors with their wives and children had arrived in the town, so Mary and Mrs. Bottrell decided that there should be a party for them. David brought back two dozen dolls from Asuncion and the wives worked hard to dress them up as presents for the little girls. Then a Christmas tree was gaily decked with tinsel and candles, flowers and presents – the first Christmas tree ever seen in Villa Rica – and so the party began. Someone was there with a camera, for faded old photographs show an array of happy faces of many different types and races, with mothers and nannies keeping an eye on the children and in the background even fathers like David and Dr. Bottrell putting in an appearance. It must have been a happy moment.

By now Mary knew that she was expecting another child, but as so often happens news came just then that David's father had died of cancer of the throat the previous October. He was just 63 and had not even retired yet from teaching. The first

David knew of it was from a copy of the *Weekly Scotsman*, which was sent out to him but which was always very out of date when it finally reached him. A few months later David's mother also died, as much from weakness and grief as from the cancer she too suffered from. And from another copy of the *Weekly Scotsman* they learned that Mary's mother, Mrs. Wilson, had died in September 1889 though they only received news in January. Suddenly all the plans which David and Mary had made to bring their children back to Scotland and to their grandparents were up in smoke. Soon the other Wilsons and Anguses were to be scattered around the world, and in that year David and Mary realised that their future lay in South America. There was nothing left to go home to in Scotland.

As 1890 wore on and Mary's expectant figure began to change, her sister Jessie finally decided to sail from Scotland. After Mrs. Wilson's death there was little reason for her to stay, with Tom and Mary both in South America. Mary was overjoyed at the reunion when Jessie arrived in June – and it was not long before the local bachelors were also showing an interest in the new arrival. As always, the Angus house was usually full of guests, as Mary described in a letter: 'It is very difficult to have a fixed time for letter-writing as you suggest, or indeed for anything with two babies who do not generally sleep at the same time, and such a constant coming and going of visitors as we have here. On Sunday I had a few minutes to begin this letter and then we had six young engineers to breakfast at noon, besides Mr. Duff who is staying in the house. Then nine more came to tea, in detachments, three stayed to dinner and for the night . . .' No doubt the presence of Jessie attracted more visitors than ever, but Mary coped with it all.

Winter in Paraguay is usually very mild, and whenever several Europeans were gathered in Villa Rica they seem to have made the most of this by having country outings or going off hunting, particularly on Sunday. David's diary several times records 'we all went shooting' or 'Rode to Cerros and got back about 6.30 p.m. Mary and Mrs. Bottrell accompanied us, over 11 leagues'. There are old photographs of wonderful picnics under trees, where elegantly dressed ladies sit on the grass around well-spread table cloths, with their escorts reclining nearby, rather like the French paintings of Fetes Champetre –

only in Paraguay everyone was properly clad! During 1890 David also had a tennis court built in Villa Rica – the first seen there, but at least another source of recreation.

On July 26th, 1890 Mary gave birth to a son called Stewart. He was a fine healthy child but of course it meant that energetic pastimes were now over for Mary. Instead the rest of the year saw people gather much more round the Angus piano, where they sang songs, or hymns on Sundays. Mary described the arrival of their piano in a letter:

'There is only one other piano besides ours in the whole place, and when we play ours we generally have an interested audience standing around our doorway, as our house is the principal one in the street. Mrs. Bottrell has the other piano and she plays very nicely and her husband sings well so we have had some nice music lately. When our piano first arrived (by bullock cart as we did ourselves) we could not use it, it was such a jangle of dischords from the damp of the journey. Luckily we found a German staying here for his lungs and he has tuned it very nicely indeed.'

Mary did not mention how well she could play herself, but many a homesick engineer's day was brightened by her Sunday teas and piano playing. Victorian 'accomplishments' for wives were of real value in these remote places. Mary had even learned to play the guitar before she left Edinburgh, in case she should have no piano in South America.

It is difficult to realise nowadays how Europeans could feel so cut off from home in Paraguay. From Villa Rica it took at least two days to reach Asuncion by train (sometimes two weeks by cart), from where it took several more days by paddle boat to Buenos Aires, and from there at least three weeks by steamer back to Britain. Sundays, when work mostly stopped, were particularly boring in a country with no recreational facilities. One old photograph labelled 'Sunday in Paraguay' shows a group of men playing cards under a cart (though David himself never played, not even whist, such was the strength of his mother's upbringing). David's diary reveals that with so little else to do some men also got drunk, but they were discharged. Meanwhile the senior engineers enjoyed the more refined atmosphere in David's house with its afternoon teas and piano soirees. One of these engineers was a Scottish New Zealander called Andrew Stewart, and who was already emerging as a suitor for Jessie Wilson's hand. As Mary had predicted, it did not take long for her sister to find a husband in South America.

Towards the end of 1890 the Anguses moved to a third house in Villa Rica, probably because of the new baby and the dampness of the previous house. This time David did all he could to make it comfortable, by laying a proper wooden floor and having proper napery cupboards built in wall recesses. He even had a bathroom added, with a tap for cold water and a slanting floor with a runaway drain so that a sitz bath could be tipped out after use – an unheard-of luxury in Villa Rica. The patio was partly roofed over and orange trees grew all around – a much better home for the family. Sadly, it proved on the contrary to be a place to great ill-luck.

First a calf died by choking on a whole orange. Then Nancy fell off a window sill and was unconscious for two days. Soon after that she ate rat poison and nearly died, and then she caught typhoid and only just survived. Then around New Year a terrible diptheria epidemic struck Villa Rica and both little Davie and Nancy fell very ill. The only account of the days which followed is a series of brief entries in David's office diary:

Monday, 5th January, 1891: Went to the end of the rails. Stopped work in rail-laying on account of the bad weather. Reached the workshops at 5.30 p.m. and found a notice from Mary that Davie was very ill and might die. Sat up with him part of the night. Andy Stewart remained to help to nurse him.

Tuesday, 6th January: Davie worse. Doctor advised to open his throat, this was done and a tube inserted. He began to get better. During the night he nearly died but rallied again.

Wednesday, 7th January: Davie getting on. Dr. has hopes for him.

Thursday, 8th January: Davie still improving. This improvement continued until the Sunday. The diary was so much an office one that there was no space allowed for Sundays, so the next entry was inserted.

Sunday, 11th Inst.: Davie began to get very restless in the afternoon and gradually got worse, unable to take food.

Monday, 12th January: Davie died this afternoon between 1 and 2 p.m. and was buried in the cemetery Villa Rica at about 7.00 o'clock at night. He was born 11th May, 1887, aged 3 years and 8 months.

Tuesday, 13th January: Cleared out the rooms with the doctor and disinfected them. Went to the office in the afternoon and got the December progress section finished and sent off. Wrote to London, to Mrs. Henderson, to Buenos Aires and to Tom Wilson. Through the night Stewart became ill with sickness and cough, decided not to go out on the line in the morning. We sent for the doctor for Stewart.

In the end Nancy and baby Stewart recovered, but to the end of her life Mary could not speak of that week without emotion. Victorian family deaths were common but she never really got over the loss of her first child, despite the other twelve which were eventually born.

It was a mercy that Mary did at least have her sister Jessie with her, for almost immediately afterwards terrible floods swept away part of David's railway and instead of staying to comfort Mary in her grief, he had to rush off to deal with this emergency. Even Villa Rica was awash and men used boats to take provisions round. Someone even saw a drowned mountain lion washed through the streets. David's diary clearly illustrates the urgency of the situation.

Thursday, 22nd January, 1891: The rain came on very heavily about 9.00 o'clock last night and continued all night with thunder and lightning ... The train cannot go out. Buchanan and Stevenson came in to tell me the line damaged at Hernandaria Bank and two new bridges of 10 metre span would be required there. Arranged with Napier to start work at once cutting up piles etc. Train to leave at 6.00 a.m. tomorrow. Still raining at night ...

Friday, 23rd January: On arriving at Yhacauguaya found that the bank on the south had been washed out for about 15 metres, we crossed the gap on the sleepers. Found 'San Pedro' (name of the engine) struck on the bank opposite Finlayson's camp. Went on to Hernandaria by trolley.

South of the bridge there, 10 metres of bank washed out, Pascoe bridge also damaged. Went on horseback to San Fransisco Station where the rails are under water too. Arranged to have drainage from Vivres land and to widen and deepen the drains from the station itself. Slept in Stevenson's house.

Saturday, 24th January: Went out to Jacami Bridge, Donald Urquhart took a photograph of the break.

The bad weather went on all through February but by March the line was almost back to normal. There were occasional accidents, as in this diary note:

Wednesday, 15th April: A. Stewart started from Asuncion with 'Yuti' (name of engine) and 20 wagons about 9.30 a.m. About 8.00 in the evening Yuti went over a cow and smashed up about 10 wagons, going completely off the line herself. One boy hurt. Dr. Bottrell and I went out in 'San Pedro' to the wreck and brought the boy in to Villa Rica, arriving about 4.30 a.m. Left Galli and big gang of men clearing the line. Napier returned with us to arrange to take out the wreck-crane and food for the men.

Later that year several engineers also died suddenly of dysentry, but mostly the work continued steadily until by June the line was completed and all that remained was to finish the various station buildings.

In June there also occurred the marriage of Jessie to Andrew Stewart. It seems to have been quite an event, with everybody travelling on the new railway to Asuncion for the ceremony. During the civil registration little Nancy, the only bridesmaid, seems to have stolen the limelight by hiding behind her mother's skirts instead of playing her part. Later at the house of the British Consul there was dinner from a table spread with a Union Jack flag. After this the marriage was repeated by a Protestant Minister, and then everyone went on a special train to the farm of Andrew Stewart's brother James. Here the couple were welcomed by James playing the bagpipes and toasted with a glass of champagne.

In August 1891 David's railway was at last officially opened. On Saturday 8th the president and vice-president of Paraguay, with their wives and a large body of officials, left on a special train calling at all the stations on the way to Villa Rica. At each place the passengers all got out and the president made a speech to open the station, before getting in again and carrying on. In Villa Rica a banquet was held in the company office and that night the entire presidential party slept in David's house, with some of the entourage in hammocks. Next morning at 6 o'clock the official train continued on down the line and the president opened more stations and made more speeches. That night another public banquet was due to have been held in Villa Rica but on the return journey heavy rain started and the guests refused to attend the dinner. Instead they all ate in David's house – how Mary ever coped with the sudden change of plan is a mystery. Next morning at 9 o'clock the inauguration party started on the trip back to Asuncion, in a better mood now despite the continuing rain, leaving David to start clearing up his office and Mary to give a sigh of relief. Though he never claimed the credit, it was almost certainly due to David's likeable, easy-going, unpretentious nature that the irritable president finally left Villa Rica in a good mood.

The making of the line, with all the difficulties presented by the floods and swamps, had been a success. In 1889 the Anguses had taken eight days to travel from Asuncion to Villa Rica by bullock cart. Now the journey took just six hours on a stopping train, though faster trains could reach up to 70 m.p.h. on some sections of the line – respectable even today.

By now David's staff was already splitting up as men went off to new jobs. David also hoped to stay on in Paraguay, for there was little to go back to in Scotland and he and Mary loved the country despite the sad memories which haunted them. As usual David had bought up several tracts of land, mostly around Villa Rica or in the chaco, and these, together with his commission on the railway and income from the line's eventual profits, were supposed to be an insurance against old age poverty. Twenty years before the first old age pensions, Victorians were still fearful of the workhouse and David wanted to ensure that something had been set aside for the future. Meanwhile what of David's next job? There was talk of surveying a line westwards through the Grand Chaco to the Bolivian frontier, but just then everything was cancelled by a telegram from London instructing David to return forthwith, leaving Mr. Duff the accountant to settle up any outstanding business locally.

David might have resigned and stayed in Paraguay, but by now it was clear that the parent company, Perry Cutbill de Lunga, was in financial difficulties, and he was involved. Timber contractors still awaited payment, legal problems still hung over railway land purchases, and now bills were coming back unpaid from London. Soon news came that the company had gone into liquidation and had suspended all payments, meaning that David and his staff would not even receive their salaries, let alone commissions or a share of any profits. The only honourable thing was to pass up the chance of more work in Paraguay and return to London to see what could be salvaged for the men on David's staff.

In October there was a last, rather subdued, fiesta and ball in the company's office in Villa Rica, and then the Anguses set off for Britain. Had David stayed on in South America, he would probably have found another post straight away, as most of his junior engineers did, but duty took him to London and in the end he never returned to Paraguay. Meanwhile, having expected a handsome commission at the end of the work, David had been spending his income as it came, and now to his chagrin he was forced to accept a loan from friends in Argentina to get the family home. He gave the Villa Rica house as security and for a time others lived there until it fell into disrepair and locals stole the roof tiles. By the 1920's the mud-baked bricks were dilapidated beyond use. The other lands, particularly in the Grand Chaco, were always expected by David's family to produce oil or minerals of some worth, but in the end they were sold during the 1930's by Mrs. Bottrell and a local lawyer for the Anguses. Sadly the price of land was then falling and they raised very little. The railway made a modest profit for four decades until a properly surfaced road was built with American money in the 1940's. Traffic switched to this road and the railway fell into a decline. It is still languishing today.

David had always hoped to come home to Scotland rich and triumphant to his parents and friends, the poor local lad made good. Although he could be conceited, this hope was not such a vain ambition, but it was not to be. In Mary's first letter home from Villa Rica she had written, 'We left the carts and walked into the Promised Land', but since then they had lost Davie-lad and their parents, they had had to borrow to come home to Scotland, and much of the promise had faded. Bad luck had over-taken them.

Chapter Eight

AFRICAN ADVENTURES 1891-1893

The Anguses reached Britain in November, just in time for a typically dull winter after five years in the tropics. David wanted to visit London immediately to see what money could be obtained from his employers, but Mary was expecting another baby so the more pressing need was just to get to Edinburgh and find somewhere to live. Mary's sisters rented a furnished house for them in Warriston Crescent, close to the family home where they had been married. And so they came back to Scotland – with no grandparents to coo over the infants, no parental fussing or sympathy as the birth of Mary's next child approached, and not very much money to live on either.

Despite the disappointments and problems on his mind, David was too much of an optimist to be troubled for long. It has long been a characteristic of the Scots that they can possess a 'profound essential melancholy of disposition and (what often accompanies it) the most humorous geniality in company,' as R.L.S. said of his own father. David fitted the same Scottish mould – easily depressed but not for long, with a wit and a conceit and a confidence typical even today.

Soon he was off on the rounds of friends he had not seen for years, visiting Mrs. Doyle, Mrs. Ryan and others. He also called on the Stevensons but by now R.L.S. was living abroad and his employers Thomas and David were dead, though the elderly Mrs. Stevenson was pleased to see him again. The younger generation of David and Charles Stevenson were now running the firm, building lighthouses all round the Scottish coast as ever. David had been to university with these two Stevensons, and he still sent them descriptions of any interesting lights found on his travels. Later David visited Robert Blackadder in Dundee, and no doubt the former master was impressed by the progress his apprentice had made since leaving him for Edinburgh University. To a man accustomed to small-time work in Scotland, David's accounts of railways and revolutions, jungles and deserts in faraway places were like the tales of a great adventurer.

Early in the new year David went to see his liquidated employers in London. Several times he saw the directors of

Perry Cutbill de Lunga but with little result. On one occasion for example, he pressed hard for an interim payment of £200, which he said he needed urgently, but he was only offered £30. Fortunately, as he shows in a letter to Mary on February 3rd, he was wise enough not to force the company into further payments, even for the legitimate income owed to himself and the workforce from Paraguay:

'It is a great shame the firm not having given us enough to live on, even for a few months until your trouble (pregnancy) has passed. The firm have no work in hand at present, there is no chance of the Asuncion job, and no chance of our being paid anything just now: if we compel them they will have to go into bankruptcy and we will get almost nothing, losing besides any interest or influence we may have with the firm . . .'

David decided instead to sail for Buenos Aires, to press the company there and, if possible, to find more work, for their money was now running low. Accordingly in February, and with Mary now nearly eight months pregnant and certain to give birth before he could return, David sailed again for South America. It proved to be a wasted journey. To begin with, the steamer took on passengers at Rio although yellow fever was then raging in the city. A woman subsequently became ill on board, so when the vessel approached Buenos Aires the passengers were all landed on an off-shore island for a fortnight's quarantine. By the time David got ashore, the posts he had hoped for were filled.

Perry Cutbill de Lunga in Buenos Aires were also no more helpful than they had been in London. (In fact it was over two years before a settlement was reached with the firm, by which David received additional shares in the Paraguayan railway, which he hoped would provide some income in old age.)

For two weeks David hung around old friends and employers, but little turned up. The most likely work was on a Bolivian railway project but David felt it would be too wild for his wife and children and he did not follow up the opportunity. Meanwhile he visited Jessie and Andrew Stewart and found them prospering in Argentina (they soon moved on to farm in Columbia, and later to New Zealand where descendants still live). David's old friend Worsoe now had a farm, and Tom was doing well working for David's old colleague Glasgow. Another old associate even offered David more money to help him over his troubles – it says much for David's friends and the high esteem with which they clearly regarded him, but David's response to this offer also says much for his character:

'Lumsden is giving me a £200 loan on the Paysandu chacra and offered to make it £400, but £200 is all the chacra is worth so I would not take any more and he will not take any interest on it. I can repay him when I get any money from Paraguay or when else I am able . . .'

Then on 23rd March, 1892, just as he was about to board a train in Buenos Aires a breathless little girl handed him a telegram which said simply 'Betty Bothwell' – Mary had given birth to a girl, but it was really the only good news on that journey. Fortunately David and Mary were so much in love that when times were bad, each could find comfort in the other – now, without work or sign of hope, this is what David wrote to Mary:

'You will be still laid up my poor old wife and I am very sorry I am not with you to comfort you in your trouble but I feel it more when I am away from you . . . I don't know how it is that I have been so fortunate as to get such a blessing in my wife, and I don't deserve it, and I have not been half thankful enough for my privileges, but I never realised so well as I do now what you are to me, and having you always with me. I did not know that it was only you who were the reason of my peace and happiness. I will try to be better to you when I have you again *my darling*. I can't imagine now how I managed to exist during the 4½ years we were engaged and while I was abroad and you were at home. I could not do it again however much I tried; away from you I am not living, now I am only trying to forget the time till I can get back to you again and everything I do or try to arrange has an eye to getting back as soon as possible, or of making sure I shall not have to leave you again . . . I don't care what happens to me in worldly matters or station so long as I have you with me and your love to cheer me. You are my world and society and everything, without you life is a blank that I cannot face . . .'

By June after a fruitless search, David was back home. As so often happens he found that a good opportunity in Turkey had been lost while he was away, as had a scheme for building a railway in Mexico. David had also been planning to form a consortium to buy and develop an estate of 500,000 acres in Sonora Mexico, at the mouth of the Colorado River, but this also fell through.

David's depressions and the constant bad news must have been very trying for Mary, but in July the Anguses rented a farm at Tullich on the shores of Loch Tay and at last began the highland holiday they had long promised themselves. With them went Nurse Jessie Graham, employed to help Mary over her pregnancy even when the Angus funds were down to very little, such was David's devotion to his wife. In the end Nurse Graham stayed with the Anguses for the next 45 years, through the births of nine more children – but her adventures and travels lay still in the future.

That summer David was hardly ever with Mary on the farm, for it was only in London that there was much chance of work. There were rumours of jobs in Chile, then Nicaragua and other places too, but they all fell through. While in London, David also visited Arthur Conan Doyle, who had moved there from Edinburgh. He mentioned this in one of his daily letters to Mary:

'. . . I have just returned from Arthur Doyle's where I took Brunner to supper. Doyle has a very nice house at South Norwood. Connie is with him but his wife and daughter (aged 3) are away at Margate. The Doyles sent kindly messages to you and treated us very well. Arthur was very much interested in our life in South America and especially in Paraguay: he had been reading "The Cruise of the Falcon" lately and was thinking of going out on a visit there sometime or other. He has given up medicine entirely now and lives by his writing which seems to pay him extremely well judging by his surrounds. They are going to Norway in August . . .'

During this visit Conan Doyle seems to have questioned David particularly on the fossilised remains of the giant lizzard creatures sometimes found in the Paraguayan Chaca, and which were evidently the terror of local natives. Soon after this he wrote *The Lost World,* peopled with similar creatures and terrors, and David always liked to think that he had helped inspire this book.

At about the same time David was at last offered a job. Two directors of Perry Cutbill de Lunga were backing, as individuals, a survey and exploration project in Damaraland, in South West Africa (the area now called Namibia). A new firm called the Railway and Works Construction Co. hoped to build a railway from the coast at Walfisch Bay to the isolated Otavi copper mines several hundred miles inland. This would involve a survey through vast areas of desert, through the lands of several tribal peoples, in a region which had been claimed by Germany, at least nominally, since 1884. In addition the company wanted an assurance that the copper mines were viable and would make the railway worth building, so a party of miners was also to be led safely to Otavi by the survey team. Having delivered the miners, the surveyors were then to return by whatever route they had found, ending up with a rough estimate of the cost of the proposed line. What was needed therefore, was not just an experienced engineer and surveyor, but someone also good at negotiations with local people, good at roughing it in the outback, capable of managing stores and finances, with courage and tact and initiative – good enough to take charge of the entire expedition. Fortunately they asked David, perhaps out of belated loyalty but more likely for his own obvious qualities. On July 7th a more optimistic even delighted David wrote to Mary:

'. . . I saw Gale this morning and heard of an exploration they have in hand in South Africa, which Gale wants me to take charge of if it comes off. I have offered to go out for £600 for five months, clear, they paying all expenses of every kind connected with the work. Brunner will go along with me as my second. It is very likely we may have to start before the end of August if it does come off, and I would have to go alone as we would be up-country all the time and going very roughly . . .'

Most of Mary's letters from this time have been lost, but it is clear that she was begging to be taken along – the thought of yet another long separation must have been very depressing, coming on top of David's constant reassurances that he would never let it happen again. David understood her feelings very well, having missed her terribly himself in the past, but he had no doubt that this time she simply could not go, as he struggled to explain in letters:

'I would very much like to take you with me, but I am afraid it would be impossible on the trip we are going. I am very sorry to have to go away again alone and do not like the idea at all of being separated from you; but I don't know what else we can do as we are now circumstanced. You see we must get some money to pay our debts and there is no hope of anything from the firm, and if we press them they will have to fail, then we would most probably get little or nothing excepting the illwill and emnity of them and of all their friends and business relations who are still powerful in the city here . . . As it is, over and above what we now have we will get £600 clear.'

The financial argument clearly did not placate Mary, so in another letter David tried a new tack:

'I am afraid it will be impossible for you to come on the exploration . . . everything will be terribly rough and in a great hurry. Then there will be no civilised houses on the road and you would not like it even if you were there. You could not go with me all the time and would be terribly home-sick for the bairns even when I was with you, but more so when I was away from you. You will just have to be doing this time, and hope it is the last, and that next spring we will be away together and can take the bairns with us also . . . There is no remedy I am afraid as we must pay our way and it can't be done by my staying at home.'

David managed to get up to Scotland briefly in August, perhaps to console Mary, but soon he was back in London collecting a small workforce and arranging for stores and equipment such as carts, rifles and saddles. Special boots and clothing were also ordered, and David's own surveying instruments had to be repaired.

David also invited Conan Doyle to go with him as expedition doctor – he said he would have been delighted to go had he not been 'tied by the leg to that wretch Sherlock Holmes' with a contract to produce a story for the Strand Magazine each month, so he could not accept the offer. If he had, he might have absorbed the background for a very different Lost World, more like that of King Solomon's Mines.

In September Mary came to London to spend a few days with David before seeing him off. David's sister Isabel and her husband were there too, and they had a day's boating on the Thames and visited many friends. It was a brief time of pleasure before David boarded the steamer *Pembroke Castle* on September 30th and sailed for Africa. Mary spent that last night with David on board the ship, and in the morning with the vessel already under weigh, she was ferried back ashore by a tug. David wrote one last letter to her and had it taken ashore by the pilot, but it was the last letter for weeks. That day as Mary returned to Liverpool Street Station, someone told her how dangerous Damaraland was and how risky the expedition was likely to be, and for weeks after she was terribly worried for her husband. By now, although she did not realise it yet, she was also expecting another baby.

On October 20th the *Pembroke Castle* reached Walfisch Bay, a small British-ruled enclave on the desert African coast, where a huddle of huts clustered round a trading post and the resident magistrate's house. This was to be the expedition's starting point. Immediately problems began – the only steam launch capable of unloading from the *Pembroke Castle* (which was anchored off-shore) was laid up on the beach for repairs. With the ship's captain complaining that he would rather drop the expedition party off at Cape Town, David took command. He went ashore, rounded up every available local man and their rowing or sailing boats, and organised the shuttle of all supplies and people ashore. It took all night, but as the sun rose through the morning mist the job was done and the *Pembroke Castle* sailed off with the expedition all safely ashore.

The party consisted of three surveyors – Angus, Brunner and Wheatley. In addition there was a separate group of about ten mining engineers, some from tin mines in Cornwall, who were to be taken to Otavi and left there to make tests. They had been recruited by an American called Copeland, but they proved to have no initiative or understanding of rough living, and throughout the journey expected to be advised and spoon-fed by the surveyors – so much so that they would even sit in a cart stuck in the sand rather than get out and help David dig it free! In addition to the surveyors and miners there were various local European people who joined the party for spells as guides or interpreters, and then there were the Germans – two German officers insisted on travelling with the expedition, and in the end they were nearly to cause it to turn back.

Germany was in the process of claiming Damaraland as a colony, having infiltrated the region first with missionaries, then troops, and later with an administration at Windhoek. The local tribes – Damaras, Herero, Hottentots, Bushmen and others – were resisting German colonisation and at this point in 1892 were actually fighting the Germans in a kind of terrorist war. This went on until 1894 when a peace was signed. White Germans then arrived, took the best land, and provoked a new outbreak of massacres and German reprisals (in one case over sixty German settlers were wiped out, but British and Boer people were nearly always left alone by the tribes). German authority was finally reasserted in 1908, but only after a 'shoot-on-sight' period of genocide by the German administrator Von Trotha. At the height of the trouble there were nearly 20,000 German troops in the field, and by the end at least 100,000 natives had been killed or driven into the Kalahari desert to perish. It was into the beginnings of this troubled period that David's expedition was about to venture.

They had hoped to start the trek inland to Otavi as soon as possible, but it was soon found that though the bullock carts ordered from London had arrived, there were no bullocks, as these had been sent inland to pasture and would take about a fortnight to be found and brought back. Frustrating though this must have seemed, it was really just as well, for the delay offered a chance to sort out several more problems and learn more of the people and their customs in the interior. Mr. Cleverley, the local Resident, loaned David maps and details of the area. David also tried to memorise some useful Damara phrases but the language was not an easy one. Another problem was that there were not enough yokes for the bullocks

– each cart needed at least ten pairs of animals, but there were only eight yokes per cart and more had to be found (these were eventually loaned by a trader and sent back to him when the going got easier). Local natives also had to be trained for chaining and levelling and other survey jobs, so there was plenty to do. The delay also gave the tiny white population more time with their visitors – Europeans were so rarely seen in this remote outpost that there was now a flurry of dinner parties and tennis matches in Walfisch Bay, as the locals made the most of the opportunity.

During this period, Mr. Cleverley took David to a native village a few miles inland. A flu epidemic was raging and had already killed many people; since there was no doctor it had fallen to Cleverley to help as best he could. David thought that the beehive-shaped native huts were the most wretched he had ever seen, worse even than anything in Paraguay, but the two men visited every dwelling, giving quinine to the patients and leaving a supply of tea, sugar, cocoa and maize flour. The village drinking water came from a central well and David watched a man ladling some into a trough for his goats. It looked horrible with a green slime on the top – fortunately David did not know then that his own party would drink such water, and much worse, long before they ever reached Otavi!

There was also time for the engineers to survey the coast for a landing place for railway construction materials. If the railway was ever to be built, a harbour would be needed. A local trader and David rode northwards to the mouth of the Swakop river, beyond the limits of British territory, where a harbour was said to be possible. The land around was fairly level, with plenty of broken granite lying about which would help with the building of the railway. David also noted that:

'. . . we should be able to make a jetty for landing our stuff at Swakop mouth, at any rate in fair weather, by running a small breakwater out along the ridge of rock to the north of the cove where the *Hyena* landed a boat last year. A proper harbour would be a major undertaking and much too expensive for the railway company to undertake.'

More ominous was a small group of German soldiers under the command of an NCO who were erecting a permanent building to live in. Throughout his time in Africa David remained concerned by the German presence lurking just off-stage, waiting, as it were, to make a dramatic entry. He wanted to show clearly to the natives that the surveyors had no link at all with the Germans, but it transpired that the miners had been told, separately, to seek the protection of the Germans if they were threatened by natives. Indeed David began to wonder who exactly was behind the mining party – the Germans may well have had an interest. They may even have been hoping for trouble, to give them an excuse to intervene. If materials were also going to be unloaded at Swakopmund, the German link would become stronger. It irritated David to feel that somehow a situation outside his control had arisen in which he was assisting the German takeover of Damaraland. Background German schemes were only beginning to dawn on him, but David could already see that he would have to give the Germans no excuse at all for a rescue mission. Somehow he would have to shake off the two German officials who had joined the expedition, and follow a policy of concilliation and friendship with any natives they came across – indeed their lives might well depend on it.

From Swakopmund David rode nine miles upriver to the Chief Constable's ranch at a place called Nxonidas, where he slept on sheep skins spread on the floor of a hut. In the morning he took observations and fixings from local peaks before returning to Walfisch Bay through a stretch of stony desert. It was a landscape typical of the interior where David and his expedition would soon have to journey, but the sheer dryness seems to have filled David with a mixture of wonder and concern, as he showed in a letter home:

'This was far and away the dreariest and most arid bit of desert I have ever seen and beats even the Mendoza deserts hollow. Today I saw no spoor of animal or bird, only a few beetles and lizards and two dead bullocks, still untouched by jackal or vulture though dead for several days.'

On November 1st, 1892 the expedition finally left Wilfisch Bay. A crowd of Hottentot boys was engaged to help as instrument porters, cooks and drivers and Arthur Gunning, the teenage son of a local trader was made interpreter and put in charge of them. Their jobs included looking after not only the draft oxen but also the bullocks, sheep and goats which would provide the party with meat on the way. And so the procession set off. It was quite a cavalcade, 'like the Israelites of old, with covered wagons and flocks of sheep and herds,' as David's daughter Louie was later to write.

By now David was also beginning to take stock of his companions. It was a characteristic that he tended to make quick, even hasty, assessments of fellow workers – his letters over the years were full of them. Sometimes events proved him wrong, but more often correct. As they set off he jotted down his comment now:

'Copeland is very good-natured and we get on well together, but he is a bit of a fraud, he gasses a great deal in the Yankee fashion but does not do much work, and does not seem willing to take much exercise . . . The mining crowd are not bad fellows, Rogers is a good man, very religious and has a good effect on the staff. I think we will all pull well together. We are to go from here to Usakhos, 97 miles away, and await there the German officers who are to accompany us to Otavi. We railway men in the meantime are going on with our survey through the mountains.'

Almost immediately David ran into difficulties. The two German representatives turned up – they were Count von Bülow and Captain Dufft, the German Commissioner of Mining in Damaraland, as he termed himself – and David was delayed in talks with them. They finally agreed to rendezvouz again further on, but now the expedition was far ahead of him. As David set off on foot to catch up he met Franz, a Hottentot boy who had been sent back to guide him – only Franz was drunk. Eventually he caught up with the carts, only to find them stuck in sand with the Hottentots all drunk and Copeland and Rogers sitting in a stranded wagon doing nothing about it. Nearby was an itinerant trader's wagon – both German and British governments had forbidden the sale of spirits to the natives, but this fellow had found a loop-hole in the drink laws by selling them Eau-de-Cologne. David organised a rescue for the wagons by hitching about thirty oxen to each cart in turn and with much yelling and whipping from the intoxicated natives pulled them out of the soft sand – a job not finished until midnight. At 4.30 a.m. the procession finally cleared the coastal sand dunes and reached the harder stoney ground of the desert. It was then discovered that one wagon was carrying three times as much weight as the others, while one had no provisions in it at all. This all had to be rearranged before they could go further. Finally they caught up with the miners' wagon, which had meanwhile kept going. They had stopped for a rest but had done nothing to help themselves, not even collecting fuel for a fire – on the contrary, they were complaining of not being properly looked after! All through his life David had little tolerance of people he thought were lazy, and now he gave these miners a real telling off, making it very clear that on an expedition like this everyone was expected to help out. In the end though, he took pity on them and found them coffee and biscuits and cold meat. The natives made a kind of porridge from Indian corn and the miners followed suit but only produced a rather watery gruel. All in all, it was quite an eventful first day on the trek to Otavi!

Over the next few days a pattern of travel developed. They moved mostly at night, or through the chill of misty mornings before a blistering sun appeared, with everyone taking four hour shifts in the wagons as they travelled. These shifts overlapped so that someone was wakened every two hours although each got four hours sleep at a time. During the day the carts would stop and tents were unfurled from the sides of the wagons to give a shady lean-to workplace. Folding tables fastened to the wagons allowed observations to be plotted and reports to be written up in something like an office. To obtain these fixings the surveyors often had to make long side tracks to local peaks or off across the bush, and all on foot, for there were no horses. Some of these observations were made at night as the wagons were moving, so there was even more ground to catch up if the surveyors were not to be left out in the open all night, though this happened often enough too.

Meanwhile the miners were still complaining about their food and the rough sleeping quarters (the same as everyone else's) and were finally asked to make their own campfire away from the surveyors, who had become tired of their moans. For the rest of the journey the miners remained a separate group, guided and protected by David, but mostly in a sulk nonetheless.

Among the surveyors, Brunner kept the wagons and camp sites well organised, while Wheatley emerged as a good cook and quartermaster. He even showed the Hottentots how to make Scotch broth and a kind of Irish stew (though sometimes with water found only after digging deep into the dried-up beds of seasonal rivers – this muddy stew must have looked revolting!).

Thirst was a serious problem with so many animals and people on the march. There was one stretch early on with no wells at all for fifty miles, while the temperature was so high that cocoa powder in tins turned to sludge and the shellac cap on David's waterbottle melted. At this point the expedition was also climbing steadily from the sand hills at sea-level to the stony table-land which covers much of Damaraland at about 5,000 feet. When they finally reached the pools at a village called Usakhos, the oxen were so desperate for water that they fought each other to get to it. After the animals had been given a drink, the men were also able to drink and wash – quite a luxury after days of dust and perspiration.

To their surprise the party found a European among the huts at Usakhos – a Dr. Sinclair, evidently not a missionary, but who had lived there for three years and was able to give them help and information. That night they all enjoyed a good dinner cooked by Wheatley – tinned mock turtle soup, fried partridges shot near the camp, liver, bacon, and a kind of apple porridge topped with a biscuity damper (it should have been pastry but was voted a great success all the same). It was certainly a great improvement on the normal diet of whatever could be shot by the natives, supplemented by tinned corned beef and hard biscuits.

While at Usakhos a native also brought the first letters from Walfisch Bay. They included two from Mary, well over a month old but precious as gold to David, who read and re-read them constantly. He wrote to Mary almost every evening, even when he was clearly exhausted, but since the chance to send letters back to Walfisch Bay occurred very rarely, they meanwhile gathered into thick bundles. As a result, Mary received them in batches of thirty or forty pages at a time. Fortunately she kept them, for they were like a diary and now they are the best account of David's adventures, more revealing than the official report which he also wrote up each day.

On Dr. Sinclair's recommendation a local native called Jonathan was engaged as an extra driver. His wages may be of interest: they were £3 per month in money, plus two sticks of tobacco, one beaker of sugar and one beaker of coffee per week, plus one pound of meat and one beaker of rice or flour per day (two beakers of meal if there was no meat).

From Usakhos a track led on through arid scrubland and spiky thorn trees. Sometimes natives with axes had to cut a way through, so that the patient oxen plodding along in their yokes could follow. The covered wagons with their ten teams of oxen cannot have been very different from those used by the Boers as they treked across South Africa, or indeed the settlers who opened up Uruguay and Argentina. All along the way there were also sharp peaks to sketch and some to be climbed for observations. Dried-up rivers had to be noted as bridge points for the railway, samples of rock had to be taken, gradients worked out and distances measured, always with a cloudless sky hanging overhead – the temperature was rarely less than 110 degrees Fahrenheit in the shade. (The climate is not usually so hot in Damaraland – David was unlucky.)

Eventually the wagons reached the village of Karabeb, where the oxen were again so thirsty that the drivers unfortunately allowed them to use the watering pools without first asking permission. This was a grave error and before long the entire party was surrounded by disapproving local villagers. Tribesmen in Damaraland, exposed so little yet to white men's way, had nevertheless learned quickly to spot opportunities for bribery – many a breach of etiquette could only be smoothed over by a gift or two, as David was to discover often on this expedition. At this uneasy point a number of tribesmen appeared with goats for sale. David's party certainly needed more animals, and it would have been prudent in any case to buy some, but a few goats were too thin and were rejected. This only deepened the offence and all the goats were withdrawn. Instead the natives angrily ordered all the men and oxen to stop drinking, and added that they would not be allowed to use the pool at the next village either. Meanwhile natives armed with clubs now joined those surrounding the party. It was an awkward situation but David ordered his people simply to ignore everything and keep on watering the animals. The villagers tried again to derive some advantage from the situation by now demanding a watering fee of ten shillings for each animal, five shillings for now and another five shillings for a drink next morning. David refused and offered only 2/6d per beast which was angrily rejected. At this point Copeland, the American leader of the miners, muttered that if this had been in Texas or Mexico, they would have taken out their rifles and watered the animals by force if necessary. Unfortunately the remark was overheard, but wrongly translated by Arthur Gunning as a threat to the natives, who became so angry that David decided to move out of Karabeb before the danger boiled over. Not surprisingly Gunning was soon dismissed as the expedition's interpreter, for 'fraternizing too much with the natives. The boy is too young and has certainly no discretion about him.'

A week later the first wagons (delays had strung them out) reached the larger village of Omaruru. Most of Damaraland was controlled by Chief Samuel Maherero, a powerful leader and one still very active against the increasing German presence, but a sub-chief called Manasse lived in Omaruru. He was the only local man who could give permission for the expedition to continue further into Damara tribal territory, for here German claims to the area were ignored and a German pass would have been useless, even a liability.

That day David paid his initial respects to Manasse, an elderly intelligent looking man, who had been village school-master before becoming chief, but who was now an invalid confined to an incongruous revolving office chair in his beehive native *werft*. 'He used to translate the missionary's Dutch sermons into Damara, but when his predecessor as chief died, he had to take over all his 45 wives and the cattle – so he gave up his Christianity in exchange for the wives and the cattle.' David found him dressed in brown trousers, a red jacket and 'a wide-awake hat.' Then Manasse gave the surveyors African names: David's height and burly frame always impressed people in these face to face confrontations, and often gave him a psychological advantage over local natives both in Africa and South America, so he now became *Katijinene* (big) while Brunner became *Okare* (tall) and Wheatley was called *Omikoto* (crooked). Permission was then given to stay in the village and

the wagons now crossed a river to the nearby white settlement
of a few houses and trading stores where they found lodgings.
Thus began a series of delicate negotiations, with not a little
diplomatic double-talk and testing of nerve and cunning and
human understanding. David was determined to reach Otavi,
but Manasse, faced with the arrival of sophisticated Westerners,
had to satisfy an understandable anti-German caution, while if
possible obtaining some benefit for his people from the situation.
They were two well-matched adversaries.

Two days later the last of the expedition carts rumbled into
Omaruru and next day the first full meeting or *raad* was held
with Manasse and his council. David described this in a report:

'The business began by his asking us a lot of questions as
to where we had come from, who had sent us, what we
were here for, had Queen Victoria asked us to come and so
on. After about an hour of this the talk came round to the
Karabeb incident and it turned out that we were accused
of having threatened the Karabeb people with fire-arms,
saying that we would take water by force. The three men
who had been sent by Manasse to look into the matter said
that this was told them by Arthur Gunning . . . it is a good
thing that we have got rid of this worthy . . . The chief then
wanted to know who was going to pay his men for their
time and trouble and I offered to do so (when they turned
up for their rewards the same afternoon they got
respectively a coat, a pair of trousers and a blanket).

After the Karabeb incident had been disposed of, the
Chief tried to worm out of us whether we acknowledged
any other ruler in the country than himself . . . He next
enquired how we had managed to get ammunition into the
country . . . We were then asked if we came to make a
living out of the minerals and if we succeeded, what was
their share likely to be. I . . . assured him that the
Company would be quite prepared to pay him something
handsome if the business turned out a success.

I asked him whether we were to be allowed to go forward
and he said yes, but that the counry was in a state of war
with the Germans . . . He also wanted to know why we had
come to examine his country without giving notice or
sending him word, and whether we had brought any

message from Queen Victoria ... Then he gave us
informal permission but said he would like to see us again
next day. He asked us again about our ammunition and
the Germans, but we were very cautious and said as little
as we could . . .'

The Victorian era must have witnessed countless meetings of
this kind between local native leaders trying to protect their
people and white men more interested in land for railways or
mines or whatever. On the one hand Manasse wanted some
kind of payment for the permission these white foreigners were
seeking, but how much was 'something handsome'? And
knowing that the Germans were also determined to take over
his country if they could, then what value English promises?
For his part David was sincere in his promises, as far as he
could speak for his company, but he could not know of wider
international events happening over his head. His job was to
reach Otavi as best he could.

The meeting seemed to have gone well and David was
pleased, but just then a new white man arrived in Omaruru.
One explorer to realise the potential of the Otavi mines had
been an Englishman called Bob Lewis; he had set up an
unofficial claim to that area and was now negotiating with
Portuguese officials to transport the copper through Angola –
the last thing he wanted was another company pushing into his
claim from Damaraland. This new arrival was Stevenson,
Lewis's private secretary, and it soon became clear that he was
out to obstruct David's plans. Chief Manasse certainly became
suspicious. perhaps thinking that David was part of some plan
by Lewis to tighten his claim on Otavi – a misconception which
Stevenson did nothing to correct. Just then word also came that
the German officials Von Bülow and Dufft were now camped
just a day's march away – David's heart sank. Manasse was
bound to rescind permission to travel on to Otavi and the whole
expedition might now have to turn back.

Ominously another meeting was called. Once again the
nationality of all the white people was questioned and cross-
examined for hours – even the nationality of their parents to be
sure that they had no German connections. Where had they
come from? Who had sent them? Was it Lewis? Whose money
was behind the venture? Was it German? Then more cross-

examination by lesser chiefs and always with wily old Manasse watching every white reaction carefully. David said as little as possible – no they knew nothing of Lewis, no they had no German links and had not asked for German protection, no the Germans had not provided them with ammunition, and so on. Several times David offered to turn back if the Damaras would not believe him, but there would have been no profit in this for Manasse and the bluff worked – permission was cautiously reaffirmed. They could proceed so long as they were not Germans, and provided that Damara warriors went with them (ostensibly to protect them from Bushmen), and that they returned by the same route, but they had to stay in Omaruru until Manasse wrote a letter of safe conduct for them and another to his overlord Samuel Maherere explaining what was happening. So far, so good, but the Germans camped nearby were still a worry.

That night 'I concocted a letter for the German officers advising them that we had had great trouble to get permission to go forward alone, and that if they came forward we might be considered a German company instead of the English one we were, and inevitably we would be turned back and expelled to Walfisch Bay. This letter was sent off about midnight by a sure and secret messenger, a step-son of Gert Struys (a local trader). He came quietly to the store and got the letter, then rode off across the river and through the veldt with orders to keep off the road and when he came up with the German wagons, to let his horse loose and crawl up to the wagon, keeping out of sight of their boys, lest they shot at him . . . He managed this all right and delivered the letter without being shot.'

Despite all this, the Germans rode into Omaruru the next day, greeting Manasse courteously enough but presumably knowing full well the effect they would have on David's mission. Almost certainly they hoped to act as rescuers by insisting that David's party was in danger from Damaras. The only result was that David was furious and Manasse became suspicious all over again. David had deceived him, he said, with such anger that the expedition was clearly in serious danger. David later told his children that the party was never closer to death than at that moment. He argued hard with von Bülow to leave his expedition alone, but it was difficult to break through the deliberate formal and aloof style of the German officers. In the end only the intervention of two local white traders convinced Manasse of the truth, and again permission was granted to journey on. The local whites had, in fact, saved their lives, a point noted in capital letters in David's report that night.

During these delays Brunner and Wheatley had been out in the surrounding bush cutting a picada or base line for the proposed railway. Mostly this involved hacking a route through thick scrubby thorns, but just as things were being smoothed out between Manasse and David, another row suddenly flared up. The surveyors had cut down a thorn bush at a corner of the church yard – allegations of desecrating ancestors' graves and the like immediately flew about, and were only placated with gifts and a bottle of whisky. Clearly the villagers were trying to wring every possible gift out of the expedition before it moved on. That day out in the bush for example, the surveyors were turned back for not giving a bottle of whisky to a sub-chief when it was demanded. Next day, a Sunday, David had to remind everyone to do no work for fear of offending the church again – do doubt more gifts would have been the only remedy.

It is easy to see the Damara people as unscrupulous beggars, or as crafty manipulators – David himself gives this impression in diaries and letters – but with hindsight it would be wrong. They were a tribe soon to be driven off their land by German colonists, taking fair advantage of an opportunity while it lasted, simply demanding payment for passing through or exploiting their territory. Today, things like blankets and tobacco sound like petty gifts, fobbed off onto innocent natives by patronising white men, but in David's case this was not so. Hard currency was of no use to Damara people, but the supply of goods which could be offered instead was strictly limited by how much could be carried in the wagons, over and above the expedition's own needs. David had to ration what few 'gifts' they had. His irritation stemmed mostly from the fact that he saw so many of his bartering goods going now, when he did not know how many landowners he might meet on the way to Otavi.

On the Monday the surveying work was completed and David went to Manasse's *werft* to bid him farewell. More presents were given – a coat and a pair of trousers – but by now the chief had discovered a fancy for David's own Henry Heath hat and that also changed heads. In later years David used to recall a story from this episode. It is not mentioned in reports or even letters but his children heard it often. It seems that David and Manasse became blood brothers, by cutting their wrists and binding them together so that their bloods mixed. It may have been an outlandish ceremony, but it must have done the trick for next day David's expedition got away from Omaruru at the cost of only a few more gifts of tobacco and drink to the most insistent hangers-on, while in the background von Bülow still gesticulated to an impassive Chief Manasse.

They had been delayed nine days, and it was to take another four weeks before the expedition finally saw the copper mines at Otavi – a month of driving the oxen to their limits and hauling them to their feet when they collapsed, of more bribes to pass through villages, and an endless catalogue of hardships and difficulties for David to tackle. The only good things were that they now had three horses on which to make surveys, and rain even fell occasionally. They also found a new guide called Jonathan who turned out to be very loyal and reliable. The people and adventures and technical work of this journey are perhaps best captured by some extracts from David's log:

30th November, 1892: 'Next day we passed through rather broken country with several rivers and streams which would have to be spanned for the railway. The line needs to keep to the north-west of the wagon road. There was less thorn and more big trees, cameldoorn principally, and aro-tree on which grows a small red edible berry . . .'

1st December: 'We reached Tatlow's store at Okovakotjavie about 4.15 p.m. . . . A man called Sabati runs this store for Tatlow, a Cape man of Italian descent. He fought his way out of Ovampoland when the Catholic missionaries were massacred. He escaped carrying his children and shooting 13 of his pursuers before he reached safety . . .'

2nd December: 'It was almost dark by the time we got back (from negotiating with a local chief). We sent up a present of rice, sugar, tea and coffee to the chief and his son brought us down a sheep as a present from them. I bought some milk for six needles. The chief will not let us go yet, he wants to see us again tomorrow.'

3rd December: 'Hyba (one of the boys) shot a springbok on

the way which the mining party appropriated. I told Hyba that in future anything that he or our boys shot belonged to our wagon, or I would not supply him with ammunition. At our midday camp Hyba and Big Bill brought along a sheep someone had given them and sold it to us for ten shillings. They wanted drink but I would not give it to them . . . however I promised them each a drink when we reached Otjipaive and another when we reached Otavi . . .'

'We arrived at Onyakava at 6.40 p.m. Tatlow began to cut branches to make a corral for his animals when a messenger came from the chief across the river telling him not to do so. After some palaver Jonathan, who knows the chief, went across to see him and I sent a present of six sticks of tobacco and a blanket . . .'

4th December: 'We were up early and taking observations from a hill about a mile from the camp. The bullocks had not appeared so we had not been able to get away. When we got back the whole population of the village, male and female, came hanging round the wagons, some of the women in very elaborate dress . . . Copeland gave Big Bill the half bottle of brandy he was promised last night, and they made a night of it, Jonathan is still half drunk. It is hopeless to give anyone drink if any work is expected of them next day. (We had) a good deal of trouble collecting up our oxen and getting them watered. They had got mixed with the village cattle . . .'

'We needed an axeman in front all the way to cut the obstructing timber, and Jonathan also goes in front to decide which is the best route . . . About 5.00 p.m. we reached a small stream with steep banks and a heavy bush, the boys cut the trees and brush for nearly an hour before we got the first cart across . . .'

6th December: 'This is a much more fertile place and there are a good many native huts about, though not so many as at Omaruru. A good deal of rain has fallen and the ground is covered with short green grass already. We propose to stay here over tomorrow to rest our oxen which are pretty well worn out . . . We put up a side tent for Hyba and the boys as the rain is so heavy, there was not much shelter under the cart . . .'

'The head man here and at all the other places round here have been warned by Kambazendi (a chief) to stop all wagons and refuse all water as an invasion by the Boers is expected . . . The whole country is patrolled by spies watching for the Boers. It seems that some months ago a party of Boers trekked from the Transvaal to Otavi, the chief man and horses going by sea to the Portuguese territory to the North. Kambazendi sent word to them to clear out and when they refused sent his son with a strong force to turn them out. The Boers went then through Ovampoland to Portuguese territory but threatened to return in force and take possession of Otavi and Groot Fontein. It is for this force that spies are out all round Otavi, guarding the neighbourhood. Hyba thinks that if we move before we have Kambazendi's permission his amour propre may be hurt and he will then turn us back.'

7th December: 'Very vivid lightning enabled us to go on for a while after it was dark, but eventually we camped or rather got our saddles off and sat on them trying to keep them dry. When the rain stopped we collected some wood and with careful nursing managed to get a big fire going, which burnt all night. We had nothing to boil water in or collect rain water, and only dried biscuit and tinned meat which I could not eat . . .'

8th December: 'The owner (of a farm) gave us both sour and sweet milk and I gave him tobacco. These huts reached close to the mountain side. We wasted some time but managed to shoot two guinea fowl and then it was a long weary ride . . . to the Waterberg which lies at the other end of the tableland . . .'

'. . . By this time it was 2.00 p.m. and we had had no square meal for over 26 hours. I was feeling as if ague were coming on again and left the meeting to try to get some cooking done. Another hour was wasted trying to roast coffee beans and pluck the fowls. It was impossible to get anything done for the crowd of loafers round us. They have been more familiar here but have begged less . . .'

9th December: 'We reached the spring and I cut ANGUS 9.12.92 on a large wild fig tree near to it . . . (Later) we met a Bushman and his wife. He had a bow and arrow, sticks for making a fire and other household traps. They told us there were lions in the mountain but they kept more to the west. Elands are getting scarce, there are also stimbok, springbok, dacja, clipbok and gambok and many koodoos. The Bushmen are intelligent looking people but not pretty. The woman had one bracelet of animal skin rings, similar to what the Damara women have in metal . . . The woman showed us a lot of roasted caterpillar kind of things which they eat. They also dig up roots and get beans from the trees. They also kill game. From each animal killed they cut a bracelet for the wife. This woman had 44 bracelets of the skins (of various animals). The things they wear are also made of skins.'

10th December: 'Went to say goodbye to the (local Damara) chief and he kept us till about 10.00 telling us of his power and greatness. He took us to his kraal to see his cattle, asking us if we had ever seen one so big. Then he dismissed us giving us his blessing which consisted of his kissing us . . .'

'We reached a werft in Omiveroromme at noon and exchanged some tobacco for a gourd of soured milk. Two hours later we reached pits with water in them from which we drank . . . As it began to grow dark we passed a werft and there an old woman showed us the way to Otjinarongo and we gave her two sticks of tobacco. My piles have been very bad and I was thankful to reach the settlement, it had been a hard gallop . . .'

11th December: 'The boys have been using too much coffee and sugar and I told Jonathan to tell them this, and then they all started complaining and said they would return to Walfisch Bay. I had to go for them pretty strong and I told Franz (one of the boys) I would send him back myself if he said any more. After the row they all worked much better . . . (Later) I gave presents to some of the men, boots and a red blanket, and I sent back half a dozen needles, some black thread and a brooch from Scotland and some women's dress stuff as I had promised for Timotheus's wife who did some sewing for me at the Waterberg . . .'

12th December: '. . . It took us over an hour to cut a way through (the thick thorn scrub). I asked Copeland to lend us some of his men but he thinks the miners are above this kind of work, and had no spare natives. So I started in myself and bossed the show, showing them how to work. It was essential to get the wagons through and the oxen were nearly played out from lack of water and it may yet be over a day and a half before we reach any . . .'

'I had given Jonathan a drink for his hard work and taking an interest in getting us forward, and Hyba thought he might get one too, but I find this power of giving or witholding drinks is the only power I have over these men, so I did not give him one as he had not earned it . . . (Later) I asked them in but they refused saying it was not right that servants should sit in the same room as masters and that they were monkeys. I told them that they were not looked upon or treated as servants and that I was sorry to hear that they were going to leave us, but about that they must please themselves. After they had left I asked Jonathan to explain to them that we were here doing work, not to enjoy ourselves, and that we could not show them the attention we would wish . . . I do not think it probable that they will leave us. In fact I think they wanted a drink, no more . . .'

13th December: '. . . Hyba and Big Bill had been out looking for water and found a little but not enough for the cattle. We made some tea with this very muddy water and had a little all round. I gave Hyba and Big Bill a drink of whisky for having found this water . . . (Later) we dug a pit in the water holes by this camp but the water put into the barrels was a liquid mud, and was still mud in colour even after being filtered. Big Bill found another water hole about a mile away from which we got better water for drinking and cooking. The last of the miners' carts came into camp about 5.30 p.m. their oxen being just about dead beat . . . the miners all riding in the carts as in the morning and in spite of the state of the oxen . . . Christophe, Copeland's chief driver had a slight stroke of paralysis this morning and is now lying waiting for mustard blisters on his feet and neck. They will have to let him lie up at Otavi till he gets over it sufficiently to travel . . .'

14th December: 'Wakened before daylight but did not rise till after 5.00 a.m. Had coffee and sardines. There has been no rain and there is no sign yet of the cattle (which have wandered off) . . . Otjenga is situated among limestone.

We out-spanned near the water which there is an abundance. Mr. Rogers got some fossil shells among the rocks ... Brunner picked up bulbs of some fine looking flowering plants, we mean to take some of them home ...

'Wheatley and I went up to high ground near here and saw all round to the north and east but we could not identify Otavi, there are a lot of hills in the direction where it ought to be. Our next water is two day's trek from here at Okhornse, and it is three days' trek to Otavi. There are some big cameldoorn trees here, some of them have gum oozing from their trunks ...'

'The gemsbok which Jonathan killed yesterday has fed the entire camp, including the miners and their boys and the men sent by Kambazenbi for dinner last night and all day today and tomorrow's morning meal.'

15th December: 'The ground has been very soft and heavy going and the bullocks have had to be rested every few hundred yards, the whips going constantly. The bullocks dragging the miners' carts are in the worst condition, the mining boys all ride as they always do and it will serve them right if they are left for a night on the veldt ... We only went about 5 yards at a time for the last hour and then rested the animals before they could go on again. I had a talk with Rogers about the miners not walking when we were in such heavy country and the bullocks so weak, but he takes the men's sides and says that they were contracted to be conveyed to Otavi and that they should be carried ...'

'There is said to be ostriches in the veldt near here and we may have a chance to shoot one. Bought a feed ox at Otjenga it cost 24 sticks of tobacco ...'

16th December: '(There is a) precipitous high mountain in front of us and we do not know yet where Otavi is ... We made up a fire and placed our blankets round it, broiled some bacon and had it with cookies made in camp this morning and a tin of potted ham and tongue. I gave the men a tot all round and we went to sleep. It was very cold and I could not sleep, I heard Bushmen talking and shouting to each other quite close to us during the night and a dog barked in the direction of Otavi.'

By now the expedition was close to Otavi, but one reason for the mine's almost mythical reputation was its very isolation. In fact its overgrown mouth was located in a hidden valley, with entrance only through a bottle-neck canyon almost impossible to find. Even now, so close to his goal, it was another seven days before David actually saw the mine – indeed he searched and rode past the entrance several times without realising it.

On December 17th the surveyors, riding ahead of the wagons, found a deserted adobe house called Thomas' Hut, with a spring nearby where they watered their horses and prepared an evening meal. By now the Damara men with them were very nervous, for they were in Bushman territory and native huts had already been spotted by the men. Then:

'. . . we were just moving our saddles etc. into the house when sounds were heard to the westwards and in a moment all the natives were inside the hut with their rifles ready, and peeping round the corners. I was writing at the time but at the cry of "Bushmen" I thought there might be danger and got behind a wall. Brunner and Wheatley were at the spring and came in just as it was realised that it was not Bushmen but an approaching wagon making the noise . . . It turned out to be Mr. Dufft, the German Commissioner.'

Once again the Germans were about to jeopardise the expedition. Dufft reported that all movements to Otavi were being stopped by Bushmen and that a force was on its way to stop David himself from working. Dufft's freight wagon had been held, Von Bülow had been intercepted, and so had David's wagon and the miners in their wagons. Dufft himself had only got through because the order to stop him had arrived too late.

By now the Damara escort was thoroughly alarmed, but David promised that 'we would protect them if the Bushmen came as well as we could protect ourselves'. Then it emerged that the order had been given by Chief Samuel Meherero, now evidently organising an alliance of all the local African peoples against the Boers, or possibly the Germans. David was relieved and knew that eventually, even if it first required bribery, he *would* get to the mine only a tantalising few miles away. The Damaras, on the other hand, became his captors now, determined not to let the white men do anything that might anger Maherero. The surveyors were allowed to hunt, and even to make survey observations, but not to approach the mine. And so the days dragged on, with David fuming at the delay but his escort steadfastly sticking to their orders. In the end David contrived a trip to the mine by ostensibly going off hunting – he did not find the entrance, but when he returned his guards were furious, terrified that he had angered the Bushmen. David's only reaction was scorn: 'It will not be very difficult to make the Damaras submit to any rule if the men we have with us are to be taken as any criterion of what the bulk of them are,' he noted dryly.

Soon the remaining carts arrived, and so did von Bülow, and now all the Europeans were clustered at a camp so near but yet so far from Otavi. They could still hunt but not towards the canyon leading to the valley with the mine. Then later the Bushmen appeared, suspicious about the Germans but not really aggressive – looking more for gifts than a fight. Meanwhile in the camp tensions grew and festered. The miners were nervous and huddled close to the Germans. The Germans were worried and wanted away, but the Damaras were letting no-one out of their sight for fear of angering their chiefs or the Bushmen. Meanwhile the surveyors worked busily on the route for a line into the Otavi valley while David wondered how to convince the natives that he had nothing to do with the Germans. In the end he befriended the Bushmen by trading tobacco for their trinkets – the one sign of clear thinking during this awkward few days.

On December 22nd a substantial force of armed tribesmen marched into the camp and that night the Bushmen leaders summoned David to a meeting. One of David's greatest assets was the honest impression he could convey to others, even if there was a language barrier – people could *see* that he was a straight talker and here it worked again. He was allowed to explore the Otavi valley with Rogers, the senior miner, but the wagons would not be allowed to follow until the Germans had gone away. And so on the 23rd, with a boy to guide them, David and Rogers set off for the copper mine. After all the difficulties of travel and negotiation David must have been elated, but his report was more restrained:

'We went up the entrance to the mine which is quite overgrown with trees and bushes but does not appear to be above 20 yards wide. We turned too much to the right on entering and it was some time before we could find the pits. At last we found some small holes, evidently some of those that have been made by the Bushmen. Mr. Rogers took me round a shaft which had been sunk by the English, probably Lewis or someone for him. It is about 30 feet in depth, not perpendicular but about 45 degrees from it in fact. The shaft is very irregular and stayed by rough timbers, if used again Mr. Rogers thinks it will all have to be properly shored and lined. I got several specimens of copper ore, Malachite (green), Azurite (blue), carbonates of copper and malachonite or Copper Glauze. The mine may be of a great value or valueless and it will require six months to determine what there is in it. It appears to me a good thing and there is another copper mine to the northward.'

Later that day the Germans were escorted away by a troop of armed men and made to return the way they had come. When they were gone, honour and reputation having been satisfied, the miners in their wagon were allowed to proceed to the mine. This part of David's instructions was now completed at last. It gave David a wry feeling of satisfaction to know that Copeland ('the most useless appendage to an expedition as can be imagined') and his shiftless miners would now *have* to fend for themselves, fetching firewood, searching for water, hunting and trading and cooking and doing all the other things they had refused to do on the journey out.

Next day the surveyors left the miners at Otavi and set off back to Walfisch Bay with an escort of Bushmen and Damara warriors. Knowing the route now, there was much more positive measuring and checking and mapping along the way, and by the time they reached Walfisch Bay a whole dossier of charts and plans was already completed. David loved the open-air life, but he would just as happily spend hours and hours drawing beautiful maps and diagrams, or making endless mathematical calculations for culverts and bridges along the route. Not many men have in their lives successfully married an urge for exploration and adventure to the patient drawing and calculation skills of an engineer, but David was one who did – and loved them both equally. Christmas Day found him up a mountain contentedly working with a theodolite – the lighthouse-building Stevensons, similar men themselves, would have nodded approvingly. On New Year's Eve it rained heavily and they all huddled in a tent with the natives and had a drink to celebrate Hogmanay.

Nights out on the veldt could still be hazardous, of course. David never properly described this in letters for fear of worrying Mary, but in fact they used to tether their horses in a group and sleep huddled into them for warmth, protected by a ring of fires. In later years David used to describe these nights to his children; perhaps his enthusiasm as a raconteur coloured things occasionally, but he often told how the Europeans and natives would take it in turns to stay awake, keeping the fires going, listening to the sounds of animals out in the bush, watching the eyes of lions and jackals glinting in the darkness beyond the flames. Sometimes the horses would also sense these animals and become restless and excited. Then in the morning they would check inside their boots for scorpions and centipedes before continuing on their journey through the dawn mists of the desert.

On the 3rd February David at last noted in his log:

'Mouth of the Swakop River – reached the German soldiers' hut about 4 o'clock or later and got something to eat and drink from them. One of them rode across to the English police hut and got our mail – letters from the Firm, Mary etc . . . The wagons came on to within a mile and a half of the German station and there stuck fast, Messrs. Brunner and Wheatley riding on here. The oxen are completely played out and cannot pull the wagon more, they have been sent back to Nxonidas for pasture. Walked back to the wagon and sat reading correspondence and papers till after midnight.'

From Walfisch Bay a coastal ship took David and the two other surveyors to Cape Town. Here David was told that the company were now thinking of surveying a branch line on the railway to Windhoek, but another letter had already told him that Mary was pregnant so he turned down the opportunity and sailed home. She had waited long enough for him already.

In 1903 the firm of Arthur Koppel began construction of the Otavi line – ironically spurred on by the German need to have military access to the sea. They followed David's route and the work was completed in 1906, at the time the longest narrow gauge railway in the world.

Chapter Nine

A COAL MINE IN CHILE 1893-1900

David returned to Edinburgh in March 1893 to a much relieved Mary. All through his absence the newspapers had been full of reports of danger and instability in South West Africa and she had worried terribly. Three months later she gave birth in the house at Warriston Crescent to a fifth baby. They called the child Mary, after her mother, but in the South American custom she was always known by the diminutive name Marycita. It must have been an anxious time for the Anguses – another mouth to feed, but no work now that David was back from Africa.

It was soon obvious that construction of the Otavi line would not begin at once and there was little point in David waiting for a post. Instead he began the round of firms in London looking for new work, preferably in South America where his heart really lay. The Anguses even moved to London, renting a furnished house in Hornsey, where Nancy was also sent to the local Infant School. She hated it there, for while the other pupils laughed at her odd mixture of Scottish and Spanish accents her younger sisters and brother seemed always to be having wonderful adventures with Nurse in Finsbury Park or on the common at Wood Green. Meanwhile she struggled on at school, only half able even to understand the lessons for Spanish was her stronger language. The teacher used to give boiled sweets as a reward to pupils who answered correctly, but in her three months at this school Nancy never received a sweet. Then at the end of the year David finally got a post in South America – not before time, it must have seemed to poor little Nancy!

The new job was as manager of a coal mine in Chile – a very profitable business in the days before the Panama Canal, when ships had to sail round Cape Horn to reach the American west coast. It was a dangerous passage through the Straights of Magellan, and the ports on the coast of Chile offered welcome relief from storms – and more coal for the rest of the voyage to California or China or wherever. Several firms were already exploiting the coalfields of the Coronel region of Southern

Chile. Some like the Lota Company were already very prosperious, producing thousands of tons and employing many hundreds of miners, but one called the Arauca Company was struggling from inefficiency and poor management. The directors in London wanted a rapid improvement of business if the firm was not to be forced out of competition:

'. . . The Directors wish you to devote yourself exclusively to the management of the coal department and landed estates of the company . . . this part of the business has not up to the present time been carried out to the satisfaction of the Directors, and they feel convinced that we have been working without proper system and economy and that great changes will have to be effected, and greater care observed in the working of the mines, keeping of stores, and general organisation of the business . . . and the Directors will expect a very general improvement under your management . . . I am particularly requested to call your attention to:–

1. The proper packing and cleansing and general preparation of our coal for market on leaving the pit's mouth. In spite of continued complaints from the Directors, as well as from our customers, they are convinced that this business has never been properly attended to, that the Company's product has been unnecessarily discredited from want of proper care in this direction.

2. Better attention should be paid to the landed properties of the Company. Although the latter are but of secondary importance, the Directors think, after you are established they will be capable of great improvement . . .'

It was easy for directors in London to demand improvements, but David (who actually knew little of mining when he applied for the job, though he taught himself rapidly thereafter) decided he could do it and accepted the challenge.

The Auguses made a last visit to Edinburgh, hopeful that this time they really would be settling in South America for good, but sorry nonetheless to leave their friends and remaining families behind. David made a particular point of seeing the Stevensons – his friend R.L.S. was in Samoa where he was to die less than a year later, but David always remembered the firm which had started him off in life. Even on the voyage out to Chile he sent them reports of lighthouses seen along the way – a small sign of gratitude to the firm which had trained him so thoroughly. Then on February 3rd, 1894 the Anguses with their four little children, Nurse, and a mountain of baggage boarded the S.S. *Ville de Metz* and set off for South America. David had a last minute meeting with the directors in London and joined the ship at Le Havre.

Just before he sailed, David was handed two documents by a representative of the company. One was a letter of introduction to the General Manager of the Arauco Company which he was to present upon arrival. The other was a private sealed letter from one of the directors (it seems the only one who had actually been to Chile), giving detailed descriptions of the company's staff, the local people who would be neighbours, or competitors or customers, and a remarkably frank assessment of the difficulties and problems in store for David. It is obvious why this was handed to him only at the last minute, for if he had read it earlier even David, for all the confidence in his own abilities, might have had second thoughts about taking on the job. As it was he had no choice now, for the ship's next stop was the Chilean port of Punta Arenas, five weeks' sailing away.

The Arauco Company owned several mines and estates in the Coronel region of Chile. These were linked by the firm's own railway, which ran past the inland town of Colico to the port of Coronel, through which most of the coal was sold. The work would therefore involve much travelling around on visits to outlying properties, or to the city of Concepcion where there were banks and lawyers. The letter of introduction suggested that the Anguses should live for the present 'at Maquegua where there is a very nice house vacant, which will, the Directors think, suit you,' but the private letter contradicted this by noting that 'this place is almost completely abandoned'. David's feelings can only be imagined.

When they reached Coronel on March 23rd, the family did not travel to Maquegua but to Colico, a much pleasanter place in the hills, set amidst beautiful scenery, but near the infamous

village of San Jose de Colico. David's letter had a comment on
this place too:

'This is a *hell* that has started up on our estate, and under
our eyes, a centre of chingana and general vice. You will
not be able to put it down, and to a certain extent it is
handy, a sort of safety valve for local vices. Old Iturra is a
sort of God there and Gracia a kind of archangel; the only
good of it is that it enables you to prohibit any kind of
trading, tresspass or encroachment on any other part of
the estate, *particularly on pay day.*'

San Jose does not seem to have been the only rough place, for
the letter went on to describe another village:

'All the inhabitants of this town are but just leaving
barbarism, they are treacherous, litigeous and untrust-
worthy, and *full of fight* but you will have had sufficient
experience with such like to know how to handle them
carefully and to avoid beginning any squabbles. The
Courts of Justice there are as they are in many parts of
Chile, a simple farce.'

Evidently David was in for quite a baptism of fire! Luckily for
the company he was a fighter too, and the letter seems only to
have made him more determined than ever to succeed in his
new job.

Of the people with whom he would soon be working, the
letter was generally favourable, but there were nevertheless
quite a few local worthies who might cause trouble, like the
man described as:

'a thorough blackguard and unfortunately lives on the
estate and keeps a store there and I believe another at San
Jose de Colico, and sells drink and robs our men at
discretion. You must not have more to do with him than
you can help, and that will be of a fighting nature, he is a
regular tintorillo.'

There were plenty more folk of the same sort, including the
'very foxy old lawyer . . . you won't get anything out of him but

you will do well to pretend to like him.' There were other eye-catching phrases, such as 'a treacherous *daring rascal*', or 'you may trust him as long as it suits *him*, and no further,' or the cryptic advice that 'you will be well to be friends with them . . .' And so the letter went on, in an kaleidoscope of local characters waiting to have a battle of wits with the new manager when he arrived.

Meanwhile the *Ville de Metz* steamed on to Chile. The ship carried lots of farm animals on board – these were kept in a compound and provided fresh food but the Angus children enjoyed watching and feeding them. There were also rats, which ran about the cabins at night; one even bit Mary's foot as she slept and another ate all the baby rusks. Then on March 8th the ship's cook died of dropsy and was buried at sea. For much of the time David stayed out of sight studying books on coal mining, but as the vessel passed through the Straits of Magellan, then a busy world shipping route, he borrowed charts from the skipper to make careful note of all the lights along the coast and sent a report of his observations to the Stevensons. Ten days later the Anguses reached Coronel where David met the present company manager and decided to take his family to the firm's Administration House at Colico.

As he had feared, David was now immediately plunged into difficulties. The Anguses arrived at Colico on Monday, 19th March, to find the miners on strike and in an ugly mood because they had not been paid for weeks. Gangs of surly, argumentative men hung around the house, many no doubt from the nearby village at San Jose. David promised to pay them on Good Friday, March 24th, but as it turned out this was easier said than done. First the books and accounts were not ready – David and the office staff were up all night for two nights straightening things out in time for pay day. (What the junior clerks thought of the new arrival can only be imagined.) Then David learned of the troops normally required on pay days at the mine – an officer and ten men were needed to help keep order at Colico, for the miners soon spent their money on drink at San Jose and fights were common.

Then Good Friday came, David's first big test of personality and authority. Here are the entries in his diary for pay day and the day after:

'23/3/94. Up all night making up pay sheets and seven time books ... Walter Jones, Alarcon, Hobson, Smith, Wilkinson and myself did the work ... The men crowd round the windows too much and we must arrange a fence in front before the next pay day to keep them off ... We began the pay about 10.45 a.m. from two windows and finished about 2.00 p.m. Afterwards we heard *reclamos* (complaints) ... a pretty rough crowd some of whom had been drinking gathered round the office window where we heard the *reclamos* and we were all the better of the soldiers, two of whom kept order. There were a great many errors in calculations and in the *vales* (pay slips); much more care is required to carry out the pay properly and we must have more time for checking the books ... From 2.00 p.m. to 7.00 p.m. we heard reclamos, many men talking loudly and rough. Found a lot of errors on account of not having books properly checked and working at such haste.

24/3/94. Men much more amenable and quiet, arranged with them quite easily, worked at reclamos from 9.00 a.m. to 11.00 a.m. The sereno from Pit No. 7 complained that Rodriguez the majordomo had maltreated him. Had him (Rodriguez) sacked and ordered away from the place. Had to go down with the sub-delegado, officer and soldiers to his house to take him away. His wife and children are left but all are to be sent off tomorrow or next day. Shawcroft would rather not have sacked him, but Rodriguez made trouble at the last pay day also, he is a talking man but a very good careful capataz when sober however he won't do here misbehaving.'

David had dealt with the miners fairly but with authority, and in one fell swoop the problem was over. Not another pay day ever found a mention in his diary for there was never any more trouble. David had a special window fitted, like a railway ticket office, with a fence to keep the men in line. The men were paid on time, fairly for the hours they had worked, and their complaints about conditions were listened to and when necessary dealt with. But from then on every miner also knew that David had a will of iron and would stand for no trouble from them.

The men must also have noticed how hard David himself worked. He usually rose at six and was at work before seven, often before the men. In the first few weeks he visited all the company's mines and properties, urging greater efficiency and better local management. There were certainly plenty of problems to sort out; for example he found that absenteeism was a serious problem – on Mondays the mines were virtually empty, but he solved the matter within a week of his arrival by paying a bonus for all coal hewed on Mondays. The arrangements for beginning work in the mornings were also changed so that less time was wasted on signing in and collecting lamps – David himself went to the mines each day at 5.00 a.m., first to understand the problem and then to ensure that his improvements worked.

Another malignant problem at the mines was undermanning. Irregular pay and other grievances were driving men to nearby rival companies. Soon after taking over David recorded: 'Only 36 men in all in the pit, day and night,' but he soon tackled this problem too. One major complaint concerned the miners' houses, many of which had leaking roofs, so David made a tour of inspection, sacked the man in charge of repairs, and sent a list of immediate work to be done to the new housing manager. David also found that women were employed in some mines, so he stopped all work for women underground and instead allowed them to do some of the sorting of coal into sizes. He even provided conveyor belts so that the women could sit down while they worked – a little touch of humanity he always felt for others. Then in April a smallpox epidemic broke out at Colico. The company was in the process of building a hospital for its workers but it was not completed yet, so David went personally to supervise the work and sacked several carpenters for being drunk instead of working properly. David's new broom worked. Within a month he was able to note in his diary, '559 men in all at the pits,' adding that 'I found the house man loafing outside the office and went for him, sent policiales (company police) to scour the place and find the absentees . . .' Within a month the mining operations of the Arauco Company had been transformed.

Now it was time to examine the firm's other affairs. This included travelling up and down the line checking all the company stores, even ordering flour personally and later having the company's own flour mills brought up to scratch so that grain could be ground more cheaply. There were also plants for making fuel bricks from coal dust and these were made more efficient. Then the supply of coal at Coronel came to David's attention – it was no use winning new orders and customers if the company could not provide a regular supply of coal for them. Coronel was a popular port for ships taking on more coal but to sell it David had first to befriend the shore agents, mostly retired captains themselves and all of them rascals 'on the make'. Here his easy-going friendly nature was a help and business soon picked up – just in time, perhaps, for in 1897 the Klondyke gold rush began and for some years lots more ships called at Coronel on their way from the Horn to Alaska in the days before the Panama Canal.

Another coal customer was the Chilean State Railway company. When David arrived there was fierce competition among the various local mining firms for the railway concession. To begin with David made contact with the local regional manager, a Scotsman called Downie; 'manager of the Locomotive and Railway Department at Concepcion. He is the man who will have to speak well or ill of your coal, and we have always found him a good friend. Do all that you can to be on the best of terms with him, and if he or his wife should go to Colico make them at home, although avoid too outward a show of friendship for the natives are jealous of him.' Whether it was Scot helping Scot, or a real friendship, or simply just good coal promptly delivered is not clear from surviving records, but David won the State Railway concession in 1898 – a vital breakthrough if the Arauco Company was to survive against its larger competitors.

Of the rivals, the Lota Company was the strongest and tried hard to obstruct the Arauco Company from expanding. From the moment he first arrived, David found jealousy and ill-feeling rampant; his instructions were to keep on good terms with Lota's English manager but in fact the two companies were sometimes little short of coming to blows. About a quarter of the Arauco Company's railway passed through Lota territory and when David first came to Chile this was being held as a kind of ransom, in exchange for which Lota wanted the right to run their trucks over Arauco rails and so lower their freight charges and put Arauco out of business. David's instructions were to use 'firmness and conciliation' but it says much for his charm and tact as well, that this volatile matter was resolved quietly.

In November 1894 the General Manager of the Arauco Company retired and only eight months after his arrival in Chile, David was given the post. It is clear from the run-down state of things that his energies and enterprise were much needed, but the appointment was nevertheless greeted with some jealousy and ill-feeling by other members of the staff. David never lost sleep over this – as usual, he had quickly summed up most of his colleagues and believed he had the measure of them all now. He had already decided who were weak, or incompetent, or too old to trouble him, and on the other hand, who were useful to keep in with or strong-willed enough to resist him. In short, he had a General Manager's flair, an instinct for dealing with people, of knowing who to ask to dinner and who to dismiss. With a few months he had made friends with all the staff, and had identified the Company's rogues and villains. From then on he remained a popular manager to the others on the staff, a man respected by the workers, and much called upon by neighbouring couples – indeed the house was often as full as in their Uruguayan and Paraguayan days, and David and Mary would not have had it otherwise.

As General Manager, the work was more varied than that of the coal manager. The company owned estates where sheep and cattle were reared to feed the workmen – these were expected to produce at least half the firm's meat requirements. David was also supposed to rear enough horses for the company's needs and regular rodeos were held to count horse heads and examine the animals. The company's railways, with their tunnels and cuttings, had to be maintained, examined and repaired when necessary. The railway also crossed the Bio-Bio bridge – in 1889 a bridge, then the fourth longest in the world, had been opened by the company across the Bio-Bio river near Coronel and David was now also in charge of this. It was quite a daunting responsibility, for the river flooded each spring with raging Andean melt-water.

David was also, of course, in charge of the miners employed at the various pits owned by the company (there were eight pits at Colico alone). They lived in rough villages beside each colliery, as miners have done all over the world for centuries, but in this case they were kept in a state of tolerable behaviour by their own self-appointed leaders. These were generally old lags, usually ex-miners, colourful characters but always of Chilean native blood, for the company did not dare appoint European supervisors to these camps. One example was Old Iturra, described to David as:

'a lazy old chap but I strongly believe desirous of acting fairly with us, he knows that he has no other future but under the company. He would I have no doubt steal a sheep or a bullock now and then or even change a bad one for a good one, but I don't see how we can do without him. You will never keep him from a private speculation but you must make him think that you believe he has no such thing on. In petty intrigues he is invaluable, knows all the ins and outs of the Indians and workmen. He was brought up on the property and I think he is a valuable man . . . Old Iturra is a kind of god here and Garcia a kind of archangel . . . Iturra and Garcia somehow or other manage or mismanage this mundolli, which you will have to lick into shape as soon as you know the ropes . . .'

Generally David controlled these men through their own leaders but there were other forms of contact with them, through their pay days, their grievances over things like housing, and their village stores, which the company had to keep supplied. David even seems to have been responsible, in consultation with the local Bishop, for appointing a priest when necessary, despite his own Presbyterian upbringing. At Colico the priest even lived in a room in the Angus house. One day this man said he would like some music in the services, so thereafter every Sunday the piano was taken from the Administration house by bullock cart to the church, where it was played by Mary. She once asked the priest for the music he wanted her to play and was told anything would do, he just felt a little background music would help the people with their prayers. So Mary, daughter of the manse at Dunkeld, sat down every Sunday she was in Colico and played her best drawing-room pieces, the Chopin she had learned in Edinburgh, and other pieces like Moments Musical, Rustle of Spring, and Humeresque. Perhaps occasionally she slipped in a few good Presbyterian paraphrase tunes as well!

Since the General Manager's job involved much more travelling than before, David now had the use of two company houses. One was at Coronel (described on page 174) and was generally the Angus family's winter residence, from where David could visit the company's wharfs and coal jetties, and also the bankers and lawyers at Concepcion (when David took over he found many law-suits on the go, mostly petty squabbles about land ownership, so he was often in Concepcion). Coronel was also the company's sales outlet and it was useful to have somewhere to wine and dine clients – since the house was the only two-storeyed building in town it was both imposing and convenient. David's children soon became used to the strange men with black coats and cigars who sometimes came to dinner.

Summers were mostly spent among the delightful hills at Colico, where the scenery reminded Mary of Perthshire and the climate was pleasantly mild. In later life Mary described her home at Colico as:

'a queer ramshackle primitive kind of house, made of wood and centred by a large billiard hall from which all the rooms opened . . . The rooms built round the billiard room reminded us of our house in Uruguay and Paraguay built round an open courtyard, and the billiard room had a glass roof so it was light enough.'

There were bedrooms along one side of the 'courtyard' for several young unmarried engineers and the local priest; life would not have seemed normal without a house full of extra mouths to feed! There were lots of other rooms too – the children's nursery, the bathroom, a company store, the dining room, the drawing room, the children's school room (they were educated by Nurse and later also by tutors), and also the kitchens, and their bee-hive ovens out in a yard. A verandah ran along one side of the house, and here the feed animals were butchered. The beast, usually a sheep, was first hung up and then had its throat cut by the house major-domo. The blood drained into a pail and was then taken over to the carpenter's shop to be consumed by all the men and boys on the estate and anyone else who happened to be hanging about – it was supposed to add to the men's virility. David's children used to sneak off to watch the men at this ghoulish feast, and sometimes they were offered a crust of Chilean-style bread dipped in the by-then jellied blood. As children they thought this a delicious treat.

The house may have been primitive, despite all its rooms, but many distinguished guests were nevertheless entertained there. It was not unusual for the Government to request permission by telegram, and often at short notice, to run a special State train along the company railway down to Colico to let important international guests see both the local beauty spots and the bustling coal mines. As the State Railways were valuable customers, permission was always given, but it meant an impromptu banquet for Mary to organise, with no freezer, no convenience foods and no idea even how many people would actually turn up. Later in life she recalled one typical occasion:

'Two warships, one Brazilian and the other from the Argentine, were visiting Chile. Advice came later one evening that next day a special was bringing a number of officers and officials to Colico. We were asked how many we could entertain to lunch, a reply was sent saying that from twenty to twenty-five people could be lunched well. Preparations began at once. The billiard table was pushed into one corner and a long horse-shoe table contrived from trestles was formed down the centre. Chairs were collected from all available sources: table cloths, crockery, cutlery and glass were commandeered for the occasion from the Tienda (company store).

Meanwhile men were sent out to the Colico woods to collect green branches and blossoms from Avellanos trees and great streamers of the red Copigues, the emblem flower of Chile. Quickly willing volunteers transformed the bare walls of the billiard room into a veritable bower of beauty, while in honour of the three nations, large red letters A-B-C were shown on a white background festooned with greenery.

In the kitchen everyone was working at fever heat. 'Don Juan', the Chileno Major-domo, butler, chief factotum and even butcher when need arose, superintended and the menu was arranged, cooked and carried out without a flaw. This was a real triumph, as although only thirty guests left Valparaiso, by the time the party reached Colico it had swelled to between fifty and sixty, but luckily plenty of food had been provided and extra tables and benches were arranged round the walls of the billiard room and everyone was found a place.

The menu began with caviare on toast as an hors d'oeuvre, and then came the celebrated national dish of Chile, Cazuela de Aves, followed by Empanados Frites the stuffing for which had been prepared the evening before by an old Chilena lady, Donna Eulalia, but there were roast turkeys too, and roasts of beef and sweet potatoes and choclas too. Sweets and fruits followed as dessert and then strong coffee, roasted, ground and served by Don Juan himself. After a short visit round the mine the party started on their long return journey to Valparaiso amidst much cheering and Vivas, "Viva l'Argentine, Viva Brasil! Viva Chile!" '

At least four Chilean presidents were entertained at the Colico house over the years, but not once did Mary's abilities desert her. To the end her husband remained personally popular with each newly-elected, shifting government, even if their politics opposed the European companies who dominated so much of Chile's economy.

On Christmas Day 1894 another baby girl was born, and was called Bell Stewart Angus. It meant a busy nursery, for David and Mary now had five children all under seven years old. Fortunately Nurse Graham proved to be an extremely capable woman and with the help of occasional local girls as nursemaids, she easily coped with the expanding Angus family.

Nurse was a typical Scottish matron with a set of rigorous Victorian opinions which would have had David's mother nodding with approval. She was short and plump, with a round face, but she ruled the nursery with a rod of iron. The children loved her, but they were just as scared of her: Nancy, the oldest, later illustrated this when she wrote:

'I used to be terrified watching the curtains when Nurse

was in the bathroom bathing Betty. I was so afraid that bandits might come through them while I was alone that sometimes I ran along the passage and stood outside the dining room to feel myself near the grown-ups who were at dinner. But I was also terrified of Nurse; when I was small I listened to hear the bath water run out and then I rushed back to be in the nursery when Nurse came for me.'

Nurse was the sort of person who believed firmly in cold baths and long walks and open bedroom windows and learning good poetry by heart and lots of other sensible things. She had a fund of old wives remedies too, and used to take the children to the Coronel gas works to sniff the tarry smell as a prevention for whooping cough, for example.

One favourite story about Nurse is still remembered by the Angus family today. Pay days at the mines were pretty rough at the best of times, but sometimes bandits would come down from the surrounding hills to rob the drunken miners of whatever they had left. One early pay day David remembered that Nurse always took the children for a walk in the afternoon, so he sent two company policemen or vigilantes after her as protection and to escort them back safely. The two men found Nurse pushing a pram with Marycita and Betty inside, and Nancy and Stewart walking alongside. There was also a small native boy who was there as a guide and interpreter, for Nurse spoke no Spanish. With much gesticulation the vigilantes tried to explain the dangers of bandits kidnapping the children. Nurse, who had only recognised the word *banditi,* asked the small boy what they were saying and he repeated that bandits were about and made a sign across his neck like a cut-throat. At that moment the two vigilantes held out their hands to help push the pram, but they looked as much like bandits as Nurse had ever seen so she took no chances and gave a mighty push which sent them both flying down the hillside. Then she turned and took the children home. Naturally enough the two men were incensed at this treatment and David had quite a job to restore them to good humour.

In June 1895 Nurse was called home for some family emergency and for a time a local girl looked after the children. This rather curtailed Mary's movements for Nurse had been so dependable that Mary had often been able to travel with David on visits to outlying mines without worrying about the children. About eighteen months later, however, Nurse returned and from then on stayed with the family to her death in 1935. Soon after this reunion in 1897, Mary gave birth to another baby, amidst special rejoicing for at last it was a boy whom they named Archie. When David heard that the birth had been successful, he wrote to Mary: 'Our bad times began with Davie's death. Perhaps our good ones are going to come in with Archie's birth.'

Things were certainly going better. The company had been profitable with improved sales and regular maintenance and sensible managing of the workmen. So much so that at about this time David started to buy shares in the Arauco Company, for he really believed in his work, as if he had a stake in the company's profits. It gave him great satisfaction to see how his hand had guided the firm to prosperity, but at the same time it must have been awkward and frustrating for a man of his temperament and natural authority to have to answer for everything to a board of directors in London. David must surely have wanted to get on with the job as he saw best, unfettered by restrictions and questions from London. In a letter to Mary he wrote '. . . I am cabling home to buy the other 500 shares for me at 5/- or under. It only means £125 more and I really believe our troubles are over.' The troubles he meant were very likely this feeling of being answerable to London. The remedy was to buy shares and have a greater voice in the firm.

Just a year later, in 1898, the great Bio-Bio bridge was destroyed in dreadful floods. As with the old Tay bridge which had collapsed at Dundee in 1879, the legs and struts were too close together. In floods, trees and other debris could hardly pass through and so dammed up a great wall of water above the bridge. For eight years the bridge had survived the Andean meltwater each spring but this time a long section was swept away, forcing the Arauco Company to build a new one if their coal was to reach Coronel. The immediate problem was to re-open the rail link to Coronel as quickly as possible, and so even while floods still raged, a temporary wooden structure was thrown across the gap. That done, David's next job was to construct a permanent replacement. He knew well the story of the Tay bridge disaster and the reasons for its collapse, for he had inspected the twisted remains of the iron stanchions himself, and had learned from the Stevensons the power of pent-up water. If anyone understood the force of water, it would have been the Stevensons, masters of lighthouses and harbour breakwaters. More recently David had also seen the impressive new Forth railway bridge near Edinburgh, built while he had been in Paraguay – indeed it was one of the last structures he had visited before sailing for Chile in 1894. Unlike the Tay bridge, its legs stood far apart, allowing the river to pass beneath unhindered. David had taken note well and the new Bio-Bio bridge, which he designed and erected with parts shipped out specially from English iron works, had well-shaped delicate stanchions through which the water could flow easily. The bridge was a triumph (David's great-nephew travelling in Chile in 1956 found it still locally known as the 'Angus' bridge), but the cost was a disaster to the company.

David may have been a fine engineer and a good manager of men, but he was sometimes unfortunately naive about the wheelings and dealings of big business. While he congratulated himself on rebuilding the Bio-Bio bridge, he overlooked the financial burden the work had thrown onto the company shareholders in London. He saw the new bridge as a chance to establish a stronger reputation and improve the company's profits. Perhaps he simply did not realise the scale of borrowing which had been needed to recross the Bio-Bio – but in London there were cynical men of business who did.

If David had any faults, other than this occasional naivete, they were that he was usually over-optimistic, and that he trusted others as much as he wanted them to trust him. If these were weaknesses, they certainly shook him now, for at the end of 1898 David learned that the company directors in London were planning to go into liquidation. The bridge was to be paid for simply by dissolving the firm, in one of those arrangements by which directors get out of debt by leaving creditors unpaid and themselves unscathed. Suddenly for all the energy he had put into his work, David's job was in jeopardy. More galling was the immorality of it all.

David's reaction, as shareholder in the firm, as manager about to see years of effort go for nothing, even as the father of children to feed, swelled up into a fury. As a younger man he had sometimes been pushed about by the might of big business, but he was older now and more willing to make a fight of it. Of course he was battling for his own job at a time when other work was scarce for a man of his age, but there was also a principle involved, the whole question of morals and honesty and the responsibility the company had for other men's lives. David argued scathingly that if the firm was in financial difficulties it was the directors who were to blame. The company's affairs were run by two separate committees, one for the mines and the other for the railways – they even issued separate shares and paid different rates of interest – but it was an inefficient arrangement which hindered the work of the general manager. This inefficiency in London was going to destroy the lives of people in Chile.

Exactly what happened after that is not clear, but in the end the company did not disappear and David kept his job. The firm was even re-organised with one committee and one kind of share. The jobs of hundreds of people survived. The financial problems caused by the bridge remained, but just then in another of the 'miracles' which had occurred in David's life before when things were bad, he now secured the coal concession for the State Railways. The contract was won against determined opposition, but it was a vital breakthrough to solvency and the financial crisis passed. It left David with a more jaundiced opinion of the uncaring men of business who could cynically ruin the lives of others, but perhaps that was not such a bad thing.

In November 1898 the next baby, Jean, was born, but then only a few months later in February 1899, four-year-old Bell died in a horrific accident. Every evening a huge jug of almost boiling water was taken to the nursery for the children's baths. On this occasion Bell ran ahead of Nurse, knocked over the jug and was covered with scalding water. She apparently felt no pain for she was paralysed and lay all night singing snatches of hymns and songs. Her five-year-old sister later recalled: 'I was in Coronel with Mama and Daddy and we went down to Colico next morning. I remember seeing Bell in her bed and Daddy crying and then the train journey back to Coronel with her in her coffin.' After this tragedy David had a bathroom added to the Colico house in the verandah outside the nursery, so that no more jugs of water were needed.

In 1900 Mary's unmarried sister Georgina Wilson arrived in Chile and spent a year living with the Anguses, getting to know the family. Her views were as firm as Nurse's and the two women did not always see eye to eye, but the children loved her. She was a typical Victorian maiden aunt – educated, very prim, unselfish, quirky and keen on botany, and quite a positive addition to the household. Later in life Marycita described what life was like with the arrival of 'Georgie':

'Nurse and Aunt G. did not get on, and they used to have terrible fights about how we were to be brought up, and this upset my mother. They must have nearly driven my father frantic between them as he always had to act as peace-maker. Finally she decided that she must have an occupation and I was selected as the victim to be taught by her, as I had not yet started lessons with our governess. Every morning I had to go to the end of the verandah in Coronel, which Daddy had made into a little study, and do lessons with Aunt G. ... She also decided that our religious education was being neglected, so on Sunday mornings she taught us the Scottish Catechism and read to us from the Bible and played hymns . . .'

Mary was overjoyed at the chance to see more of her sister, but for David the arrival of Georgina offered a chance for some teasing and a little bravado. To him, Miss Wilson was a weakling from the city, a fish out of water in the roughness of rural Chile, so he took her on hair-raising raft expeditions on the Bio-Bio river and insisted that she learn to ride. It was all fun, even if only to David, but to her credit Georgina did not once back out of the adventures so thoughtfully provided by her mischievous brother-in-law.

The fashion for coming out to South America seems to have caught on, for while Georgina was in Chile, brother Hugh, the 'baby' of the family, got the chance of a gold mining job in Bolivia. Perhaps he was following the example of David's original journey to Brazil, for he too left a fiancee in Scotland to earn a fortune first in South America. Hugh Wilson's adventures are another story, but in 1906 his last letter reported that he had saved over £1,000 and was coming home to get married. Some time after that he was murdered in a remote part of Bolivia, but it was weeks before anyone in the family knew – Tom Wilson was in Santiago when he heard, but by then it was too late and too far away for him to find out properly what had happened. Hugh Wilson's body was never recovered.

It is worth adding that David's brother Duncan also came out to South America, during the 1890's. As earlier with John and George Angus, David was anxious not to be seen showing too much favouritism to his brother, but he did try to find him work with other people, as this letter shows:

'Mr. Walker asked me this morning whether I thought Duncan could manage the superintendence of the construction of a railway a little to the north of Iquique, about a year's job (about £300 per annum) and prospects of a much larger and more important line to build when this one is completed if he gives satisfaction. It is probably Duncan's opportunity and if he will only go for it properly, if he gets the job he will be made. His mistake here has been that he has not been solid enough in acting on his own judgement, that is, he does not study the matter enough when he has to decide for himself and prefers acting on others' suggestions. In his new billet he will have to act for himself and on his own responsibility – Duff (another of David's old friends) will always be within reach to help him by advice in a difficulty, but Duff's value does not lie in Engineering, although he manages men well . . .'

Duncan seems to have got the job, but such temporary work cannot have been very satisfying. By now Coronel was bustling with ships heading for Alaska and the Klondyke gold rush; with the town full of eager prospectors all believing they would soon be rich, it was not long before Duncan caught gold fever and in 1898 he joined one of these ships. With brother William now running a silver mine in California and David mining in Chile, it almost seemed the natural thing to do. David later wrote:

'I am very glad Duncan is going to get clean away . . . if

things do not go on improving and we have to go, better that Duncan should be entirely independent of us. I will give him instruments which he can pay me for later on . . .'

Eventually Duncan reached the Klondyke, but in 1911 he was murdered there in mysterious circumstances. The family never found out what happened, but it is extraordinary how several men from two very ordinary Scottish families were inspired by David's example to go out into the world and find adventure.

On June 23rd 1900 another baby girl was born at Coronel to Mary and David. She was christened Georgina in honour of her aunt, but was always known as Joy for short. That made a family of seven surviving children, two boys and five girls. It was quite a handful but between them Nurse and Mary managed. The older children certainly loved Chile and the rather rootless life they had been born into. It must have been quite confusing to learn of distant Scotland and hear gentle highland lullabyes, knowing you had been born in a place called Uruguay or Paraguay, and that you lived in Chile where you spoke Spanish; but between them Nurse and the Angus parents provided quite enough stability and protection and love and happiness. Indeed at a time when children in Britain were expected to be 'seen but not heard', David happily doted on his children and was much more tolerant and broadminded.

In 1899 for example, they celebrated Queen Victoria's diamond jubilee by going to the theatre in Concepcion and even staying the night in a hotel there – quite a thrill for the children, and the sort of treat that would stick in their minds for years. That was a special occasion, but it was normal for the children at least to go fishing or boating on the lakes around Colico, or riding on David's trains, or having picnics and parties and lots of plain good family fun.

They were educated too, mostly by governesses such as Miss Priscilla Millar from Coronel (although she was afraid of bandits and would not travel to Colico). Another was Miss Rachel Elder from Edinburgh, who stayed for two years and became great friends with Nurse. (Nurse's diary shows how lonely she often was for people who were her personal friends and not just Angus family friends: she never learned to speak Spanish and so could not converse with local people, even the

Angus housekeeper.) The governesses were useful to begin with, but eventually a time came when a more formal education was required for the older children. As a result, when Aunt G. returned to Scotland in 1900 it was decided that twelve-year-old Nancy and ten-year-old Stewart would travel with her and attend a proper school in Britain.

Chapter Ten

LIFE IN CHILE 1900-1909

In later 1900 the RMS *Oravia* left Coronel for England. It was a tearful farewell as David and Mary with their younger children watched Nancy and Stewart sail off with Aunt Georgina. At that time the voyage home took about six weeks, but it passed safely and soon the children were living with their aunt in Edinburgh. Mary took the parting very emotionally, and from then on was liable to fall into a melancholy depression whenever she thought of her distant children. Nancy and Stewart, however, adapted quickly and happily to their new circumstances, as generations of other young children have also had to do when sent away to school.

During the weeks when the children were still sailing home, Mary often played 'For those in peril on the sea' on the piano. The coast of Chile was certainly a notorious graveyard for ships, but unfortunately just at that moment there was another wreck. Two officers, the only survivors, came to stay the night at the house in Coronel – in later life Marycita could still remember how they sat crying in a corner, telling of the women and children, including their own, who had drowned. The effect on Mary must have been awful, but eventually the letters and happy descriptions of life began to arrive from Scotland and the worst at least was over.

Nancy attended the Ministers' Daughters College in Edinburgh, as her mother had done before, while Stewart went first to Blair Lodge school and then to Edinburgh Academy when he was old enough. Robert Louis Stevenson was educated there, which may have influenced David's choice. It says much for the impact that Scottish education must have had on David and Mary, that they sent their children from the other side of the world back to Scotland to be properly schooled – and at such a heavy emotional and financial cost.

Fortunately Aunt G. was good at making the children write lots of letters home. Over the next few years a steady stream of mail flowed out to Chile, some to the other Angus children but mostly to Mary. When letters came Mary would read them out to the family, often with tears in her eyes. On Sundays there was the usual gathering for family hymn singing, but now with streaming tears Mary would play 'God be with us till we meet again' and other heartrending Victorian hymns – for all their talk of duty and courage and a stiff upper lip, the Victorians were also more emotional and melodramatic than today.

In 1901 yet another baby was born in the house at Coronel – a boy whom they called Donald. By now a problem had arisen, for that now made four children who had not yet been baptised. One of these was Archie, now four years old – he had actually been sort of baptised already by the priest in Colico, when he was ill once and it was thought he would not live through the night. David and the priest were great friends and as a result none of the usual Roman Catholic promises were asked for in the hasty baptism of the dying child. In the event Archie lived but the priest was disciplined for his omissions in the service and was sent to a monastery in the Andes never to be seen again in Colico.

This time it happened that the Anglican Bishop of the Falkland Islands was visiting Coronel, so David asked if he would christen the children properly. As Aunt G. had seen for herself, life in Chile had made the Anguses much less Presbyterian and more easy going than she approved of, even to the extent of having a priest living in the house at Colico; David and Mary were nevertheless still Calvanist enough to wince a bit at the pomp and ceremony of a full Anglican service, so the bare minimum was requested. In fact the Bishop used the entire Prayer Book Service, including a promise that the children would later be brought for confirmation, which infuriated David and started a row. To make matters worse, little Archie lay on the floor and kicked and screamed during the service, shouting that he would not let 'the clown' put water on his head – presumably he meant the Bishop's mitre and robes, but the unfortunate cleric can hardly have gone off in a good mood. Later a Presbyterian minister visited Coronel and the children were all baptised again, in Archie's case, for a third time! (The christening robe used on these occasions was one made about 1858 for the Wilson family; it has been used often since then, and has been sent all over the world to the christenings of Mary's and all the other Wilson grandchildren and great-grandchildren.) Tragically Donald died of meningitis at the age of only ten months. His death was especially sad for David, who had so much wanted lots of sons. Three daughters were yet to be born but they all grew up with the feeling that they 'ought to have been boys', though their parents loved them as dearly as their other children.

For much of the time, especially in winter, the Anguses lived in the Administration House at Coronel. It stood in a wonderful situation, with just a beach of dark volcanic sand between the house and the Pacific Ocean. It was actually a flat above the town's railway station, and later in life the more mischievous children used to tell people that they had been 'born on a railway station in South America'. The house was quite large and modern, with up to date plumbing, gas lighting and a glass enclosed verandah running all round the rooms – there was even a cobwebby wine cellar. Inside, the house (already furnished but not entirely to Mary's taste), was typically Victorian, no-where more so than the drawing room festooned with red velvet and gold damask curtains held in place by gilt cherubs. There were Greek pillars and painted flowers, aspidistras and photographs – indeed it might have been any Victorian middle-class house had it not been for the shelves of odds and ends gifted to the Anguses by ships' captains who had been to dinner.

Inland from the house the rest of Coronel rose up a hillside of shanty houses and muddy streets. An open sewer meandered all through the town before passing by the end of the Angus garden to discharge into the sea. When Nurse took the children for walks she made them spit after crossing the bridge over this drain, in case of typhoid fever. In spite of these precautions, however, and constant vaccinations, the children several times suffered bouts of typhoid.

Despite its ramshackle appearance in parts, Coronel was a bustling cosmopolitan town rich with the languages and faces of sailors, settlers, merchants and adventurers from all over the world. The Angus's shoemaker was Basque, the chemist was Portuguese, and the baker with his daily cart of delicious crisp bread was French. The local store was kept by a German, the doctor was Spanish, and the children's blue sailor suits and white pinafores were made from material bought at the draper shop of a Frenchman known as 'Ellisaitch' (though perhaps these were only his initials!). There was also a bar at the nearest street corner to the Angus house, where an Italian organ-grinder often played, complete with a monkey which collected centavos from the crowds. Sometimes Welsh or English employees from local mines also came to town, so that together with David's broad Scottish accent, Coronel must have been quite a colourful place.

The streets were especially interesting. Near the Anguses was a row of little houses where, in good weather, old ladies sat at doorways making pillow lace and occasionally sucking maté from a pot kept warm by charcoal. Sometimes there were fights when the pubs came out at night and now and again the children were able to watch – the spectators usually made a ring in the street below the housekeeper's window. Evidently no holds were barred as the men, stripped to the waist, 'went at one another like things demented, once even biting an ear off!' according to Marycita. The railway station itself was also a focus of some interest, especially when a train came in from Concepcion (the nearest large town, about an hour's journey away). Then all the senoritas would arrive in their powder and paint to saunter up and down opposite the station, to be seen and to see what excitement might have arrived from Concepcion. At night the Angus children could see these girls getting ready on the verandahs of the shanty town behind them; beautiful ladies dressed in finery, brushing their hair and sometimes washing it – usually in a po! Then when they had been sent to bed the children would listen for the two policemen who walked around the town at night, signalling to each other on bone whistles and calling out 'Todo sereno: siete hochos' (all clear: seven o'clock).

Early in the new century the first cinema appeared in Coronel. It was called the Bio but the Angus children remembered it later chiefly because in the first film, a jerky silent French picture of ladies in Victorian dresses, it showed rain coming on – whereupon the audience got up and ran off for shelter!

Sometimes there were religious feasts and processions in Coronel, often unintelligible to the Anguses but interesting nevertheless. Brightly painted and dressed statues of the Virgin were carried through the town, and older women appeared all dressed in black with shawls or mantas on their heads while the young girls were dressed in white, with white veils. On other days there were happy fiestas, when girls in colourful dresses with wide skirts would dance in the open air to a guitar or a harp while the men sat around in a circle clapping their hands and singing. A favourite song whistled or sung by everyone was 'La Paloma'.

The eighteenth of September was Chile's National Liberation Day and was always a great feast. Everyone dressed in their best clothes and there were speeches from important people. On this occasion the Anguses usually went to Colico, where hundreds of people, the miners, their wives and families and everybody else would have a party, with drinking and dancing until well into the morning. (David and Mary continued to celebrate Chile's independence for years after they returned to Britain, even long after the First World War.)

One of the biggest fears in Coronel was of tidal waves and earthquakes, hence the reason for almost all houses being single storeyed. Years before, there had been a very bad tidal wave at Concepcion – a children's tale said the original town was now under the sea, but that if you rowed out at low tide and put your hand down into the water at the right place, you would be able to feel the top of the old church spire. It was only a story, but David's children were young enough to worry that the same might happen to Coronel, so he told them that if a tidal wave ever did come, their house would simply float off the top of the station to land safely on one of the islands out in the bay, just like Noah's Ark on Mount Ararat. This reassurance worked so well that Joy actually prayed every night for a tidal wave, just so that she could watch the house float off!

More serious were the earthquakes which quite often hit the Coronel region. Small tremors were so common that everyone was used to them but there were also stronger shudderings enough to damage houses. On one occasion a small American stove which stood in the corner of the nursery and had a long iron chimney going up through the roof, was shaken loose and toppled over. Hot burning coals spilled all over the floor and were only extinguished when maids rushed in with pails of water. During another tremor the glass in a large drawing room mirror was smashed, but Mary replaced it with a Milais print of Cinderella and life just carried on.

In 1906 there was a much more serious earthquake (the same

one which destroyed San Francisco in California) and which Joy later described:

'We little ones were in Colico with Nurse, but Archie, who was ill, was in Coronel with our parents. Before we went to bed Nurse took us all out to see the sunset sky. I don't remember what it looked like but I do remember all the servants praying and talking and saying it might be the end of the world. In the morning, of course, all was rumour and various walls were bulging or cracked and things had fallen over. We were so young that we had not been frightened, just pleased that we were allowed to stay up a little longer than usual and excited by the bustle among the grown-ups, and when Nurse shepherded us in to bed we went to sleep and slept through it like tops. Nurse must have been very brave for we had no inkling that she was apprehensive though everyone must have known an earthquake was likely. When at last news came through from Coronel on the telephone we heard about the bad earthquake further north (at Valparaiso) but all the family in Coronel were safe. Later we heard how our Uncle Tom Wilson, Mama's brother, had been in a hotel which had collapsed in the night and many people had been killed or injured. Uncle Tom was left with nothing but his night-shirt and he caught pneumonia. Though he recovered from that it brought on the consumption from which he died some years later. He probably had carried the germs in his body from Dunkeld manse (where his sister Agnes had died of TB as a child).'*

Now that some of the children were growing up a little, Nurse began to change too, and to reveal some lovely endearing characteristics. She had, for example, a private horror of bats and used to tell the children awful tales of bats becoming entangled by their claws in people's hair, and how the hair had then to be completely shaved off (this worried Marycita especially, for it never occurred to her that the hair would ever grow in again). One day a bat got into the nursery so the

---

*David's brother James was caught in the same earthquake at San Francisco, but survived.

children, convinced by these warnings, took shelter under the bedclothes while Nurse suppressed the terror she must have felt and fought the creature with a broom. As a result, the children tended to jump involuntarily and put their hands over their heads at the mere sight of any bat. Nurse also told them of a man who died of a wasp sting on his neck, so that at the sight or sound of any wasp the children would go about with their hands clasped behind their necks! And there were lots more tales of warning, including that of the lady who died from drinking water with her soup, or the lady who broke her neck because she brushed her long hair upside down and swung it back with too much force. Mary and David must sometimes have wondered just what went on in the nursery!

Of course they knew full well that in Nurse they had a treasure, and indeed she lived with the Anguses until her death. Long before they needed a governess, for example, each child could read and write well. Every day after tea Nurse would also read to them from good but challenging books such as Robinson Crusoe, Pilgrim's Progress, Swiss Family Robinson or Children of the New Forest, and each new story by E. Nesbut as it first appeared in the Strand Magazine. On walks, especially at Colico, she introduced them to the creepers and ferns and fungi of the pathside, so that from an early age the children knew all about which wild berries made the best jam, what could be eaten raw, where the tastiest nuts grew, and so on.* In Coronel walks meant visits to the park and a host of happy games such as Puss-in-the-Corner, or fishing for tadpoles in the pond of the main town plaza (though Nurse never forgot also to take the children occasionally by the graves of Bell and Donald, where they sometimes left wild flowers, and a wreath on All Saints Day).

Unlike many Victorian children, the Anguses were never just 'left' with Nurse. Occasional breaks away did make the parents more tolerant and gentle when they were with their children, but there was always a full and happy family life. Almost every night there was singing around the piano, when David would perhaps march up and down the corridor in Coronel with one of the toddlers on his shoulders, singing 'The march of the

---

*Nurse learned about Chilean plants from the eminent American botanist Nathan Banks, who stayed for a time with the Anguses in 1894 and often went riding along the local pathways.

Mulligan Guards' and other stirring songs. The children also learned 'Songs of the North' and many more Scottish ballads and Jacobite songs, for David was anxious that they should know of their 'home' far away. They certainly knew the songs of Robert Burns more thoroughly, and at an earlier age, than children in Scotland – but that has often been the way of the expatriate Scot.

David especially enjoyed being and playing with his children when they were inland at Colico. Here there was more freedom to come and go, less need to dress stiffly, more scope for adventure. Sometimes David and the children went riding together, dressed in native ponchos and 'looking like the horsemen in the Apocalypse' as Marycita later recalled. If necessary the youngest travelled in pannier baskets slung on each side of a donkey but as soon as they could walk the children were also taught to ride. The girls rode side-saddle just like adults. Riding was an enjoyment special to David and his children; Nurse had not ridden for years, the governesses rode too gingerly, and Mary had stopped riding years earlier when a fall gave her a double hernia, so here was one favourite way by which David cemented a great bond with his children.

The children also enjoyed rowing with their father at Colcio, where there were a number of artificial pools built to provide the house and railway with water. On Sundays especially they would go rowing or bathing or picnicing – a pleasure made temporarily more difficult by Aunt G.'s stern disapproval of such frivolity on a Sunday, but which was revived when she left in 1900. There were also tennis courts at Colico. Though he was growing older and heavier, David enjoyed playing with his children, for as with riding Mary could not participate.

There were other less vigorous pleasures, however. All the children learned by the age of ten to play chess. It was an interest David had maintained since his university days, and one he considered a necessary part of his family's education. He was also fond of springing little surprises on the children, as on the day when be brought a mysterious large washing basket into the nursery. First he summoned all the children, then he opened wide the verandah windows, and then the basket – a cloud of little birds flew out! David had bought the birds at a market from people who would otherwise have eaten them – a fair amount of thought and effort for just a moment's pleasure and delight before the birds fluttered off to freedom. One little bird was actually left behind with a broken wing but Nurse looked after it until it could fly again, when it was also released. After that it often returned to the nursery to be fed, although the children had a theory that it was actually to visit their pet canary!

The Angus houses were always full of pets. Besides the canary there was a watch dog at Coronel and occasional other creatures too, but Colico seems to have been a vertiable menagerie. At one point Jean had a fox terrier, Joy had a full-sized poodle, and there were at least six other dogs also there at the same time including a Skye terrier and two great danes! Meanwhile there was also a cat, which lived in the nursery and had kittens regularly in the cupboard there, not to mention a number of half-wild cats and kittens which lived in the rafters of the billiard room skylight. These cats were tolerated because they caught the rats which would otherwise have infested the nearby Company Store. As if all this was not enough, the Angus children at various times also kept pet donkeys, rabbits and even deer, all cheerfully accepted by their parents. It illustrates, perhaps, how tolerant David and Mary were of their family's activities, but there were rewards, for the children quickly learned kindness and developed a sense of responsibility and caring for other creatures.

One of David's favourite treats was to take the children with him on the railway engines, when inspecting the coal mines around Colico for example. Archie actually learned to drive a locomotive before he was aged twelve, by which time he was also going into the pits with his father, absorbing from him the work of an engineer and manager. Sometimes the girls also rode on the engine footplate, and Joy later recalled these happy railway journeys:

'We went from Coronel to Colico by train and sometimes in winter the bridges would be washed away and we would travel in the bogeda (wagon) behind the engine to the broken bridge, then cross the river in a rowing boat and find another engine and bogeda waiting for us. I remember once that two bridges were down. We travelled in a party with parents, Nurse and nursemaids and very often visitors and their nurses too. We stopped at all the stations and Daddy often got out and bought us cherries and peaches and paper streamers and butterflies and birds cut out of coloured paper. These we hung out of the windows by their strings fastened to sticks, and they looked as though they were flying.

Sometimes the train went off the line and we had to wait for ages and that was an adventure too, especially when it got late before we reached Colico and we began to think of bats and bandits. We once saw a band of murdering bandits being taken off by the police. Once we had a really bad smash, an engine crashed into us from the rear. I remember Daddy stood up and looked out of the window at the back of the sort of observation car we were in, and turned to Mama and said, "It's the end, Mary". I thought he just meant the end of the train but a moment later we were all thrown over and the seats and furnishings were on top of us. No one was killed but the nursemaid had a bad cut on her head and Daddy had a very nasty leg, black and blue all the way up and it was weeks before this was better.'

If a train was derailed, a gang of railway workmen had to be called out, but Joy's worry of bandits was very real as she sat in the coach with evening creeping on, awaiting help. Chile was a land of sharply contrasting living standards and great poverty, where death could come very suddenly and bandits were still common. The road from Colico to San Jose was dotted with wooden crosses put up as penances by murderers who had confessed to the priest – each cross meant a murder. Sometimes the foreign managers of mines were killed by locals who resented their wealth – the English owner of a mineral mine further north was killed, together with his bodyguard of government troops, when miners attacked them – but just as common were the periodic revolutions of the ordinary Chileans. These did not usually entangle foreigners but they could become accidentally caught up in bloodshed. At Coronel during one revolution the children saw four men shot dead by soldiers on the beach in front of the nursery windows. On another occasion David came back from Concepcion on the 5.30 p.m. train covered in blood. The man sitting next to him in the train, a Mr. Scroggie who is supposed to have been mixed up in some revolution, had been shot dead through the train window, but the bullet had also taken off the edge of David's ear so that he returned home with blood streaming down his neck! Word of this incident must have leaked out, for news of the death of David Angus was reported in newspapers and then copied by the English press. Soon there were anxious telegrams from Scotland to know if this was true – to judge from surviving letters, David still had a surprising number of real friends in Britain despite his long absence from home. After this episode David always carried a loaded pistol in his pocket, and by his bed at night. Mary was terrified of firearms but she carried two strong hat-pins in her bag and a bottle of pepper to throw into the faces of any attacking bandits. It is doubtful if these would have been very effective but it illustrates how real the possibility of violence or murder was in Chile.

Though David certainly knew how to enjoy himself, most of the time he was very busy on company business. The coal trade was a precarious one, for the favours of important customers, even the government itself, could swing suddenly from one producer to another. The Arauco Company was never powerful enough to have real friends in high places. David himself had an engaging personality and he did sometimes provide almost lavish hospitality for influential people, but these things had only a limited effect for there were other firms with expense accounts just as lavish. Important people also rarely survived long in office before being ousted by revolution or assassination, so coal companies often had to begin again, cultivating new contacts and influence.

The coal business itself was also a fluctuating one, thrown about by the shifting tides of world trade. There were times when, having built up coal-producing capacity, trade then fell away and business slumped. When David took over the mines in 1894 they were producing 50-100,000 tons of coal a year, but by 1909 this had been increased to 250,000 tons a year – indeed David reported that he could have reached 500,000 tons had there been a market for so much. Unfortunately the market was such a variable thing that David was sometimes obliged to sell off surplus stocks cheaply – to the consternation of shareholders in London, who perhaps did not appreciate the difficulties of day-to-day business when presented with only an annual report. For David it was an unhappy Hobson's choice – if he did not expand, he might lose markets when they arose, but if he did built up supplies and markets did not appear he would be left with unsold stocks. He would then either have to sell at reduced prices or else reduce output again by laying off miners – men who might go to other companies and be difficult to replace.

Quite apart from the ever-present search for coal markets (especially in view of the financial situation after the reconstruction of the Bio-Bio bridge), there was also the question of the Arauco Company's railway. Since other firms paid for the use of this line, without which trump card the company would surely have been taken over, this was a source of revenue almost as important as the coal itself. Here again David faced a delicate dilemma, caught between the shareholders in London who demanded high tariffs for rival firms, and local Chilean pressures – rival companies with political influence, radical newspapers such as *El Mercurio Santiago*, and popularity-seeking politicians looking for a reason to throw out foreign-owned companies. In the end David sided more toward the shareholders – the tariffs *were* high, for the need to make a profit was important at a time when income from coal was unreliable, but it stirred up a hornet's nest among local farmers and businessmen who complained that such high charges on the only existing railway were pushing them to ruin. This in turn led to anti-British press campaigns and more than one government debate in Chile. It must have been an unenviable responsibility for a man like David with a conscience.

The railway also required regular maintenance, and between 1900 and 1905 a lot of work was done to improve it. There were, for example, thirteen tunnels on the line to Coronel; all of these were completely relined by workmen. (Two of the tunnels were christened 'Jean' and 'Joy' after David's daughters, a typical Angus touch.) There were also a great many wooden culverts, built to conduct water under the railway line; almost all of these were replaced, as were all the wooden aquaducts, which were rebuilt with bricks and masonry. Two wooden railway bridges at Camarpargue and Curanilhue were also replaced. Another problem was that much of the track ran along the very edge of the coast, where it was sometimes flooded or damaged by the open exposure to north-west gales. David had ten kilometres of sea wall specially built along the most windswept stretches in a major undertaking to protect the line. It was all ceaseless, demanding work, quite apart from the everyday supervision of the mines and farms and the coal trade.

Of course there were also customers, the day-to-day visitors to Colico who still had to be entertained – railway people, shipping people, politicians, all expecting David's usual genial welcome and Mary's unfailing hospitality. Sometimes it was a happy reunion of old friends but always it was another demanding occasion, reflected perhaps in this terse note of 1902: 'Dear Mary, I will be up this afternoon. Tea immediately. 4 people. You must be civil. Yours David.' The Anguses knew well that in these fluctuating times, every customer counted. Their very way of life in Chile depended on it.

In 1904 David's sister Isabel sailed out to Chile for a visit. It is almost as if those on both sides of the family wanted to come and see for themselves the near-utopian way of life David and Mary enjoyed – a reaction somewhere between admiration and moving in on their good fortune. Despite the difficulties of David's work, the Anguses certainly had an enviable life style – two houses in contrasting scenery, housemaids and servants to do the work, an income of over £1,000 a year, and even a whole railway system at their disposal, including a state coach for travelling from Coronel to Colico. It must surely have impressed the rest of the family, and it is little wonder that in later life the Angus children described their carefree days in Chile as undoubtedly the happiest of their lives.

When Isabel returned to Scotland some months later, however, she took with her Marycita and Betty, two little girls aged only eleven and twelve, destined to join Nancy at the Ministers' Daughters College in Edinburgh. They never saw Chile again. It was a particularly painful wrench for their mother; Mary was expecting her eleventh child and must surely have felt a terrible anguish, seeing her surviving children one by one reach the point of youth, only to have them whisked away from her by a ship to England. Marycita, a particularly sensitive child, also felt the parting cruelly, deprived of the give and take of her siblings and the reassuring love of her parents at such a special time in life when so much was new and changing. 'How could my kind parents have done this?' wrote another Angus daughter in later life, reflecting the bewilderment they felt when taken off to school in Scotland.

In 1905, perhaps as a consequence of these heartbreaking separations, the entire Angus family sailed to Britain for a holiday and a joyous reunion. It was the first holiday David had taken since becoming manager of the Arauco Company in 1894, but it was not entirely for pleasure purposes. It is clear that a small but articulate number of shareholders in London were unhappy about the erratic returns on their investments and there were also accusation about the running costs and management of the company. Typically, David decided to confront these people face to face at the 1905 annual meeting of shareholders.

Wisely he put pleasure before business, for it would have upset Mary dreadfully had he brought her to England only to dash off with her to London, with all the evenings of worry and doubt which that would have caused. To be fretting for her children, yet obliged to reassure her husband and support him as their very future hung in the balance, would have been intolerable. Instead they arrived weeks before the shareholders' meeting and went straight to Edinburgh, to showers of kisses and hugs, and gasps of pride and admiration to see how attractive Nancy had become and what a fine young man Stewart was. It was a *much* better way to begin their visit!

For a time they rented a farm at Dunkeld, but later David took his daughters on a tour round the places of his youth, while Mary happily visited friends and relatives she had not seen for many years. Each day letters came, charting the family's progress as they explored Findhorn and the highlands and the faraway places David had talked of in Chile. Now all those Songs of the North became clear – there really had been a Bonnie Earl of Moray, and there were the hills of Clan MacGregor. It must have been a happy time indeed for David.

Soon after this the Anguses travelled to a farmhouse at Giggleswick in Yorkshire, where Mary's sister Jane lived with her husband Andrew Little, a Bradford ear, nose and throat consultant. Now, while the rest of the family played and explored in that oblivious way of children, David went to face the Arauco shareholders in London. It is clear that there was a great deal of canvassing and lobbying going on behind the scenes prior to this meeting but David wisely did not get involved, and in the end he emerged bloodied but still manager in Chile.

Much of the criticism concerned the sale of coal at low prices made necessary by previous over-production. No shareholder likes to see profits lost unnecessarily, but after a typically frank explanation of the difficulties he faced, David was exonerated by the board of directors. The Chairman, Sir Robert Harvey, seems to have been particularly sympathetic and '. . . does not seem to attach much blame to me for what had happened,' as David wrote to Mary that night. Later in life Harvey in fact wrote several generous testimonials for David. On the other hand the board had also to think of the shareholders and some gesture had to be made to those who wanted action. As a result, when David, now sure that he would not lose his job, tactlessly asked for a salary increase, this was bluntly turned down – he could continue at the same rate or resign. His contract was extended, and his commission on the sale of coal was helpfully increased, but as David wrote to Mary, 'I am afraid if we were ever to have a very bad half year at any time there may be a chance of our losing the appointment'. And so, as the Angus family dragged themselves away from the four children who were to continue at school in Scotland, the position was clear. David would carry on as manager but he was expected to produce better, and more stable, profits. From this time on, the relationship with London began to deteriorate, for it was clear that the shareholders were concerned only with themselves and had little interest in the difficulties David faced in winning for them their profits.

When he returned to Chile, David tried hard to improve his share of the coal business. A greater number of visitors than ever were carefully cultivated and profits did indeed grow. By 1909 David was able to report a regular annual profit of about £70,000, with gross capital of over one million pounds – quite a substantial company. In 1907 the firm's wharf at Coronel was extended by 75 feet to allow larger ships to collect coal directly, rather than have it shipped out to them in the bay by lighter boats. It was a considerable construction project – at the pier head, several cast iron cylinders each four feet wide had to be installed to support the heavy steam crane required for transferring coal into the ships. The new pier provided a water depth of 25 feet (33 at highest tide) but even that was only achieved by carefully manoeuvering huge thick timbers fifty feet long into position and then ramming them into exactly the correct place – imagine the shouting and sweating which must have accompanied even such an ordinary engineering job! And all with David in the thick of it, hoping that here perhaps lay the answer to his sales problems.

Unfortunately the London directors of the company seem to have taken a more active interest in David's work after the meeting of 1905 – unfortunately, because while they may have been good directors, they were not salesmen. By interfering in the work they had employed David as an expert to undertake, they sometimes over-reacted, as shown in this circular printed by an angry shareholder: '. . . In December 1906, and January 1907, when the price of ordinary 2nd class Chilean coal at Coronel, which is the seat of the Chilean coal trade, was 23s 6d on shore, the Directors made a contract with the Pacific Steam Navigation Co. for 100,000 tons of coal at 16s, delivered alongside ship, which would be equal to 15s on shore, and in January 1907 they made a contract for 10,000 tons with the Kosmos Co. at 17s 6d delivered on board and bunkered, which is equal to 16s on shore, and that these prices had no warrant, were most unfair and lost the company at least £50,000.'

Criticism of this kind prodded the directors to take new action, so an agent called Edmondson was sent to Chile to take control of the marketing side of the business, just as David had once arrived to relieve the previous general manager of the coal mining sector of the company. The significance was not lost on David, who felt understandably insulted, especially when it transpired that Edmondson was also authorised to inspect all the company's books and expenses, as if David had somehow been dishonest or wasteful in the past. He had certainly been obliged to provide sometimes generous hospitality to potential customers, just as his rivals did, but when the company accounts and even Mary's private domestic books were later inspected nothing was found out of order. Nevertheless the very fact that the Anguses had been scrutinised at all was hurtful and the damage was done. Relations with London continued to deteriorate.

During these years after their visit to England the Anguses tried hard to settle down again in Chile, but the atmosphere was changing. In 1907 and at the age of 47 Mary gave birth at Coronel to her twelfth child, a girl named Louie (the story of her name is given on page 21). Then in 1908, to the great surprise of everyone, yet another girl was born, and christened Helen. Poor David! All these girls when he so much hoped for boys. Perhaps this growing family was a symbol of putting down roots, a gesture of intent that they really hoped to continue living in Chile despite their problems, but in fact the birth of more children was not enough to settle the future.

In 1907 Nancy finished her schooling and returned from Scotland to the overflowing joy of her family, but even this may have had an unsettling effect. With Nancy home the house was full of fun – she was beautiful and cheerful and exciting, and young men were forever asking her to parties and dances and tennis – but she made the others realise how much of a backwater they lived in. Her modern wardrobe of Edwardian fashions was like a wedding trousseau to the others and made their clothes look so dated. She brought with her new songs and games all the rage in Europe but unheard of in Coronel. She had been changed by life in Britain and unconsciously brought the seeds of more change to Chile. Certainly when the break came, it made the parting and the return to Britain easier, for Nancy had shown what they were missing in Chile.

Undoubtedly business was the biggest cause of worry. Letters to the children still at school in Scotland paint a picture of hopes and fortunes rising and falling like a tide. In May 1906 David wrote to his son Stewart a letter bubbling with optimism:

'You will have seen from our letters that we have had a tremendous struggle with a native coal company, the shares of which are mainly held by members of the family of the president and other influential Chilenos. Things looked very critical for us for a time but I am happy to say that we have come out on top, very much on top in fact. If things go on as they are doing we should clear over £100,000 net profit for the year. £39,000 is the amount required for interest on both classes of bonds and amortization. Six weeks ago we were selling coal at 12/4d. In Coronel Bay our last sale of 14,000 tons was at 27/– and we have sold in all over 12,000 tons at an average price of 20/9d. The trouble caused by the fight of the State Railways against us is by no means over, in fact affairs are in such a state in the North about Antofagasta and

Iquiqui that there are grave fears of a revolution breaking out there . . . '

David was, of course, prone to moments of blind optimism even against the reality of events – it is the same national characteristic which takes Scottish football fans to London every two years even now – but Mary was more pragmatic, as in this letter to her daughter Betty:

'Try not to spend your money on useless things or things you can do without, as we may be very hard up one day. The letters from London are not at all encouraging and we are feeling *very* anxious just now and not at all sure that we will be here much longer and if you get into the way of being careful and considering how you can save your father, and give him comfort also in your good reports, you have no idea how much you may ease the heavy burdens he is carrying just now.

Poor old Daddy! All the time he is so thankful and happy that we had such a nice trip home with you all before the anxieties began. That seven months with you all can never be taken from us and will be a happy memory all our life.'

In 1908 Archie, now a boy of eleven, was sent to join his older brother and sisters in Scotland. For a time he had boarded at an American college in Concepcion, but he was unhappy there and often ill. By now he was really too old to keep on having a governess, so in the end it was thought best he should go to Edinburgh. He sailed from Coronel with a family called Walker, friends of the Anguses who had a son Archie's age and were also going home. The parting nearly broke Mary's heart but it also had a painful effect on the other children, as Joy later wrote:

'We missed Archie dreadfully, especially Jean who was very near him in age. We felt we would never see him again and when we walked to the end of the mole with Nurse we used to sing "Will ye no come back again?" What a sharp sorrow children feel . . . '

Peggie also wrote of Archie's departure:

'After Archie had left us for school, as we were returning to Coronel from Colico in our sumptuous "royal" coach, we were involved in a dramatic accident, everything in the corridor carriage collapsed. I was under a seat. Our father injured his leg . . . my sister Joy was in tears. Was she hurt? everyone asked. "It's Archie," she moaned, "How miserable he will be to have missed this!" And how we all missed Archie, our only remaining Chilean brother. Stewart, about seven years his senior was already at Edinburgh Academy. A favourite walk of Nurse's when we were in Coronel was to the end of the "broken mole", a derelict loading pier which stretched well out into the Pacific – or so it seemed to small children and we had to be helped or carried over the worst parts. How vast and boundless was the ocean and yet somewhere beyond the horizon was my brother. I clutched the ancient railings and Nurse clutched me to prevent me falling. I shouted with all the strength of my infant lungs, "Archie, Archie! Will ye no come back again?" . . .'

From this time on, the family were so unsettled that the end of their stay in Chile became only a matter of time. Mary longed for her absent family. The children still in Chile became divided between those who knew and remembered their older brothers and sisters, and the three youngest girls, the 'spoilt brats' who did not. David was also unsettled, partly by the impracticable suggestions he kept receiving from London, but particularly by the presence of the agent Edmondson. By 1909 he began to look around for another job. In his heart he wanted to resign immediately, but at the age of 54 this was not something to be done lightly, certainly not without having another post already arranged.

David's age was undoubtedly a problem. Managers' posts were rare but he could not accept a more junior post, for his age would have been awkward among younger men, and it would also not have paid so much. There was one hope, for a new railway was being planned across the Andes from Argentina to the Coronel region. David knew the area well, and he even had an optimistic interview with the Chilean President about it.

Even if it meant returning to Argentina that would not be so bad, for David still had contacts in Buenos Aires and he could set up there as a consultant engineer. Eventually he applied for the post of observer to this trans-Andean line, but the letter was still being considered when a new argument with London finally broke his patience.

It was a small enough matter – trouble caused by a disgruntled employee who had been sacked by David and gone home with a grievance to London – but David felt that the directors did not support his actions and he resigned as manager of the Arauco Company in Chile. From Santiago, where he was now an accountant, Tom Wilson urged him not to resign until the Argentinian post was secured but David went impetuously ahead and his request was 'accepted by the company with much regret', as Sir Robert Harvey later wrote in a testimonial. It is doubtful if Harvey meant exactly what he wrote, however.

The news spread like wildfire throughout Colico and Coronel, as shown in a letter from Mary to David, who had gone off on another business trip:

'After your train left yesterday Mr. Hodgson walked up to the Ulloas with us and on the way we met Mrs. Franklin, Miss Dora Cooper and Cecil. We found the Ulloas in and we all did a weep! They are coming to see us one day in Coronel before we leave. When leaving there we met Mr. Aspillaga looking very young and fetching in a frock-coat. He was *very* nice and sympathetic and said the Arauco Company would *never* get another man like you, no matter how good the new man might be. He said he had no fear of your future, that competent, straight men like you were not so common and that it was only in time of adversity that the real men showed up; that all men were alike when in good times and successful, it was only when trouble came that the real man came out. He said stranger things had happened than that you might be back here again, although he was afraid you would be snapped up and "enredado" in the Argentine. So keep up your spirits without that one in your bag which I am sorry I put in as you are man enough and far better off without it.'

David *was* depressed, and sad at the thought of leaving the places he had known for fifteen years, where his children had played and he had worked so hard. He did remain a shareholder with the company to ensure an income for the future, as if he at least believed that his work had been worthwhile and would see the firm over this rough patch. The company even retained him for a nominal fee of £100 a year as an advisory director on Chilean matters, for his contacts and knowledge of people and places were vital, but later in 1909 the time came for the Anguses to leave Coronel.

At this point details of the trans-Andean railway had not yet been finalised, so it was decided to sail meanwhile for Scotland and return later if necessary. Mary, Nurse and the five youngest children boarded the R.M.S. *Oravia* for home, but David and Nancy took a different route. Hopes of the Andean line were still strong, and so was David's old adventuring spirit, so he and Nancy took a train high up into the Andes and there, where the line ended, they hired mules and crossed the mountains to Argentina following the route David thought the railway ought to take. Their adventures on this journey are another story, but eventually they safely joined the *Oravia* at Buenos Aires and together the Anguses left South America, with no idea of what lay in store for them now.

Chapter Eleven

THE TWILIGHT YEARS 1909-1926

The return to Britain, though it had something of a homecoming about it, was nevertheless an unusual event. On the one hand David could be seen shepherding his family of toddling girls off the ship, and yet the casual bystander might well have thought that at his age David was coming home to retire. To his youngest children he did indeed seem more like a grandfather than a father.

Before long it became clear that David was not going to get the trans-Andean railway job – the likely reason was his age, for while he may have *felt* strong and full of vigour, his heavy middle-aged frame did not necessarily *look* suitable for the harships of rough work high in the thin Andean mountain atmosphere. In fact David and Mary never did return to South America; not to their house in Paraguay, nor to another post in Chile, nor even to that consultant engineer's office in Buenos Aires. Perhaps the casual bystander would not have been so far off the mark, for in retrospect those last years of David Angus' life *were* a kind of retirement, certainly a time of busy work but really just to tide him over until the call came for him to return to South America. He waited and hoped for years, until he knew that he was too old and would never work again in the places he had loved.

But all this was for the future. In 1909 David was a man full of zest and confidence, fully expecting to be back somewhere in South America before long. He had a vision – David Angus and Sons, Consultant Engineers, Buenos Aires – a firm which would busy itself with the multitude of engineering schemes still open to people of drive and enterprise in Argentina. The plan may have received a knock when it became clearer that the trans-Andean railway job was not to be, but it was thought only a temporary set-back and David fully believed that something would turn up. Indeed the steamer tickets which brought the family back to Britain specifically included a concessionary clause which said they would be treated as part of return tickets if used again within a year – such was David's confidence.

To begin with the Anguses went to Edinburgh, where they rented a furnished house in South Oswald Road near the

Blackford Hill, in a suitably middle-class suburban part of the city. There was no need to buy a house because David did not expect to be there long enough to justify it. When no immediate work in South America materialised, however, the need to find a temporary post in Britain arose and now David was in a quandry. He had hoped to settle somewhere in Scotland, either in a village convenient to a mainline railway, or better still, on the Moray Firth where he had grown up. However it was clear that David's experience was most likely to obtain work in London and reluctantly the family moved to a furnished house in Muswell Hill, at that time somtimes known as the 'Scottish Quarter' in London. Soon David obtained an office at 37 Old Jewry in the City, and here he set himself up, he thought temporarily, as a South American advisor and consultant.

He was not short of employment, for there were plenty of old contacts and colleagues glad to see him back among them, and who put work his way. Sometimes it was only advice they sought, on the geography or political situation or availability of materials in various South American countries. David kept up to date by maintaining a wide correspondence with friends and officials still in South America, for he was good at cultivating and keeping ties with people. Just as now, they often had a knack of coming in useful at some unlikely later date. Sometimes these contacts in South America also produced work – typical of this was the ordering and checking of rail track, much of which was made in Yorkshire and had to be inspected by David before being shipped off. Sometimes these rails were ordered from foreign countries and at least once, in 1912, David made a lengthy visit to Berlin.

From time to time proper schemes came along. David worked on the Buenos Aires to La Plata electric railway, basically a subway line but with elevated sections in some places. He also designed the Buenos Aires to La Plata electric tramway, a railway from San Nicolas to Rufino Station in Argentina, and several railways in the Corrientes district of Argentina. Dreams of a trans-Andean line also came true, and by 1915 David had helped with plans for a northern trans-Andean line from Copiapo to Tinogasta, a southern trans-Andean line from Loncoche, and with reorganising the Chilean Eastern Central Railway from Brazil to Lebu. He also worked on a report on the coalfields in the Arauco region, and on a report on distilling oil from lignite and coal in the Coronel region. It was work, but somehow doing it from a London office was not really as satisfying as being out there, doing it on the spot.

In 1911 David was invited to be an advisor for the Railway and Works Company (the people who had sent him to Damaraland, and with whom he had kept in touch). This led to him designing a railway from Manaus to Itacoratiara in Amazonia, the Alajuda-Grecia electric tramway in Costa Rica, and producing a report on oil bearing lands in Ecuador. Some of these works were never built, because of the outbreak of World War in 1914. None of the works which *were* built have David Angus' name on them today, but they made a modest income for him at the time.

Just occasionally something different turned up. In 1910, for example, a man called Jones came to the house to demonstrate a new automatic by-pass for lighting gas lamps, especially street lights. About this time the Stevensons were also working on automatic lighting devices and David must have been aware of the potential for the future. In addition, this man also suggested that they call his lighter the 'Wee MacGregor', but perhaps this was just a salesman's inspiration, playing on David's interest in the name. In any event David put quite a lot of money into the venture, and lost it all. Fortunately he accepted the ups and downs of fate, especially those of his own making, with a philosophical resignation.

Work was inevitably fitful, especially to begin with when David was not yet well established as a consultant and ventures such as the Wee MacGregor did not help. But there were other sources of income which were enough to allow the Anguses to live modestly. David's associate directorship of the Arauco Company produced a small sum, as did most of the railways which he had helped build, and for which he had always retained shares. In addition, before his marriage David had been obliged by Wilson family lawyers to take out numerous life insurance policies, which he had kept fully paid up over the years, even when finances were extremely low. It was a typically Scottish precaution, and a wise one, for now these matured at suitable intervals, very often just when a lump sum was most needed, as in 1917 when daughter Louie needed a hernia operation which cost over £100 (Mary suffered from a double hernia for much of her later life, but there was never enough money to have this operated on as well). Later still the Anguses had good reason to be thankful for those canny Wilson lawyers of a generation earlier – one insurance policy, for £1,000, was tied up so that it could not be borrowed or realised until David's death – it was, in fact, all that Mary had when her husband died. Nevertheless, before the First World War there was enough income for the family to live quietly in Muswell Hill and even to pay for a daily maid. There was, of course, no luxury like a motor car but there were occasional holidays for the children to cheaper resorts like Southend (David's brother James had meanwhile become a millionaire in America and now sent £13 every year to be shared between the unmarried daughters – a curious sum, but it helped to pay for their seaside holidays).

Nurse lived with the family too but although she did the cooking and housekeeping she stoutly refused any payment, saying that life with the Anguses had become her home. David left her some money in his will but when Nurse died years later this sum was still untouched in her account and went to her heirs.

It was, of course, David's regular consultancy work which mattered most, and which was depended upon for much of the family income. Precise examples of just what David was up to during this period are rare however. Many of his plans were traced onto linen, as was normal then, but during the Second World War when material was scarce most of these were boiled by his daughters and reused as handkerchiefs and nappies! No doubt the need must have seemed great at the time, but sadly the evidence of David's work has therefore disappeared down the drain.

Apart from finding work, another early priority was to get the family settled into schools. This was not a problem, for the pattern had already been established during the Chilean years. The girls would go to the Ministers' Daughters College in Edinburgh (Nancy had already left and was now doing a secretarial course, but Betsy and Marycita were still at school), while the boys would continue at Edinburgh Academy, boarding with Aunt Georgie as before. Soon Jean was sent to the Ministers' Daughters College, but Joy was too young in 1909 and had to spend a while at local private schools (there was no junior school in Muswell Hill) before progressing also to Edinburgh. This regular renewal of extroverted, worldy-wise Angus girls must have been quite an experience for the staff at the M.D.C. especially when told that there were still more from the tribe yet to take their places. It was also a considerable sacrifice for David and Mary, but one which they accepted gladly, and at least Edinburgh was much nearer than it had been in Chile.

Despite this, the three youngest girls probably got the best education of all, for until the age of seven, when they went to a local private school, they received a personal schooling from their mother and Nurse. It was many years since Mary had ever taught but she still had the gift and as a result they could all read and write easily long before they ever attended a 'proper' school – although just to have lived in that stimulating house would have been education enough. Eventually Peggy and Helen went on to the North London Collegiate School where the fees were paid by Nancy (see page 209). Louie, however, was just the right age when David's friend Charles Challen, the piano manufacturer, offered the family a place at Christ's Hospital at Hertford, a charitable foundation where he was a governor. She attended from 1916 to 1925 and has described her years there in *Blue Skirts into Blue Stockings* (1981), a colourful volume of recollections.

After school, Marycita went on to the Edinburgh School of Art where she took a diploma in 1914. Meanwhile Stewart moved on from the Academy to Edinburgh University where he took a degree in Engineering – the vision of David Angus and Sons was growing stronger. David was, of course, pleased to have his son at university for it established an academic groundwork for the future, but ever since his own days at the same university he had retained an even stronger belief in practical work, and so Stewart was enlisted, like his father, as an apprentice with the Stevensons. The family firm was still going strong, building still more lighthouses round the Scottish coast as the pattern of shipping and trade changed, but still also working on a grand variety of other engineering schemes. David and Charles Stevenson still ran the firm much as their father and uncle had done before and it was not difficult to have Stewart taken on to the staff with them. So now began that same thorough training which David himself had received from

Thomas Stevenson a generation earlier.

David also looked up his own old task-master, Robert Blackadder in Dundee, and this letter survives:

> 'Dear Angus, I am pleased to see your handwriting again – it was always very neat and it stirs old associations which warm my old bones. I am now an old man – verging on my 80th year and practically out of business as my memory, hearing and eyesight are bad, or rather failing, and I am very breathless, so much so that I have been detained in the house for the last week or two, altho' I have no pain or trouble. I would be very pleased to hear from you how the world has used you . . .' (and he goes on to say that he understood David had gone to India).

Life in Edwardian England was something new for the Anguses, as Nancy had shown it would be when she returned to Chile in 1907 full of modern ideas. In Colico they had lived rather cut off from most world events; David's brother George was wounded fighting the Boers but even this long war hardly intruded into their lives, certainly not as Mafeking did in every British household. They returned to a world very different from the one they had last known properly in the 1880's. Now it was a land of Suffragette women campaigning for the vote and a popular Liberal government determined to help old people and the unemployed. The discovered fears of civil war in Ireland, and a Labour Party already growing at Westminster (when they left Britain for Chile the Labour Party had not even been born). Trade unions were also growing and huge strikes were all the news in popular newspapers like the *Daily Mail*. It was all very new; there was much to readjust to, and in fact David did not like all that he found in Britain. Even the neighbours seemed to be so formal and disapproving. It was one thing to *visit* England, as he had done in 1894 and 1905 but it was quite another matter having to *live* there. The Anguses never really settled in London, as shown in a letter by David as late as 1925 where he wrote:

> 'I hope we all go to Brazil soon . . . we have never really taken to life in this country after South America.'

Some aspects of Edwardian life did, of course, meet with their approval. Mary had sacrificed a teaching career to marry David and on the whole she applauded the Suffragettes with their incessant cries of votes for women. Indeed, when Louie was first sent to a local private school, they sent her knowing full well that the headmistress was a keen Suffragette. The whole world of careers for women was yet to open up but Mary, even set in her middle age, supported women's rights and David supported Mary – later most of their daughters made careers for themselves.

On the other hand the wider world of British politics was too different now for David to enjoy it any more. Life in Chile had been largely outside politics – British politics were too distant to matter, while Chilean politics did not extend to foreigners, so they had lived in a sort of vacuum, only to return to a Britain with many of the old political faces gone, giving birth instead to death in Ireland and Labour M.P.s at Westminster. Meanwhile time and responsibilities had mellowed the radical views of David's youth and he now voted Conservative. Feelings of humanity and social justice were as strong as ever in David but he could not reconcile Asquith's Liberal government with the unprecedented growth and power of trade unions, whose long and bitter strikes hit so hard at ordinary working people, in his view. (More than one letter mentions that the Anguses were sometimes short of coal, for example.)

As an employer in South America, David had managed men with his kind of benevolent paternalism – there had been no word of trade unions and even strikes had been rare. In David's view his had been the correct way to manage. This new world of socialists and growing union power was foreign to a man not slowly conditioned by the years to their development. It was too sudden a change and he never forgave the Liberals for 'letting Britain go to the dogs'. To his death he retained a passionate anger against Lloyd George as one of the younger Angus daughters later wrote:

'My earliest political memory is of drawing Lloyd George being hanged, after hearing my father let off steam about him at breakfast. We had no idea who Lloyd George was – I was about 4½ years old!'

(In the 1920's David's daughter Peggy formed a great friendship at school with Ishbel, the daughter of Ramsay MacDonald. She subsequently became a socialist and joined the Labour Party. This led to flaming political disputes with her father, but since both were Scottish and also Anguses, they were arguments which they both probably secretly enjoyed.) Just as many families coming home from colonial life in India found life in Britain difficult to accept, so too did the Anguses.

There was, however, the sanctuary of the house at Muswell Hill. For several years, until the Angus girls grew up, private domestic life was not so very different from life at Colico or Coronel. There were not the same Chilean surroundings, but family life itself was a joy to David, a wonderful pleasure after a day at the office. The atmosphere of togetherness, so strong in Chile, still survived. David often took the girls on treats, as he had always liked to do – in 1910 on the day before the coronation of King George V, they all went into central London to admire the decorations, and every year on November 9th he brought the family into his city office so that they could watch the Lord Mayor's show from the window. Sometimes they went boating on the lake at Alexandra Palace while on Sundays David usually took his family walking out over the golf course at Muswell Hill, in the days when people did not play golf on Sundays. David even had a tennis court laid out in the garden of their house where, as at Colico, he played with his family.

Every day, like a never-failing ritual, the girls went with Nurse to the woods which still grew all around their home, places like the Highgate and Queen's Woods where plague victims were buried in 1665, or the Coldfall Woods which belonged to the Church Commissioners, from whom any family could obtain a key for £1 a year. Here, among the oak and hornbeam and lime trees they collected brambles and built wigwams and made ponds and waterfalls by damming little streams. Sometimes, when woodmen were thinning the trees, they collected wood chips for lighting the fires at home. Alas, the Coldfall Woods are now mostly built over.

Every Christmas, when they were all home for school holidays, they also put on a play 'for good causes like Dr. Barnardo's and the Red Cross' as Louie later recalled:

'One year it was the Water Babies – it took in all our ages

and we only needed to enlist the help of two friends to make up the whole cast. The next year, 1913, we did a musical called Baron Bold the Smuggler, and again we were all in it. We acted in the drawing room and invited friends and neighbours in to watch. In some ways we were rather like the Bastables in the E. Nesbit books, except that we had grown-up sisters too, and Archie who was an awful tease.'

It was a happy, carefree yet regular way of life, with lots of fun to make childhood a wonderful memory yet enough discipline to make the children feel secure.

Although they adopted many outward appearances of normal English life, David and Mary were not really very Victorian at all. Their adventures abroad had made them much more tolerant than, for example, the other Wilsons or Anguses, who were often shocked at the much more relaxed attitudes to life shown by David and Mary. One strong memory of many people raised in middle class Victorian or Edwardian Britain is of the strong discipline maintained by every father in his own house. In Scotland a leather belt hung behind many a kitchen door and was used hard and often, but there was no such belt in the house at Muswell Hill. Louie later wrote:

'I can't remember many rules or rows about what we did. In those days there was a general acceptance of what was *comme il faut* – and as long as we were reasonable and helpful in the house there were few reasons for rebellion – though we all argued . . . In the last resort my father was very much in control, but he was always working in the City, or if he was at home, then in his study. Physical punishment was *never* used. 'No jam for tea' or 'early to bed' or washing one's mouth out with soapy water for rudeness!'

It is clear that an important difference between David and many another father of that time is that he did things *with* his children. He was their friend as much as their father, an accomplice in their adventures and a willing listener to their stories. They shared interests together, such as photography – so much so that they had their own dark room in the house.

Certainly the children were sent away to schools in Edinburgh, but David had been there too as a little boy and he knew that they would survive, and maybe even find their feet sooner. But perhaps he also understood what it was like to have a distant father, for his own father William had disappeared for years just at that time in David's life when a boy needed a father to grow up beside. It is not the sort of philosophy David was ever likely to write down, but it is so obvious that he tried to be different with his own family, to live life *with* the children when they were around him.

And yet there was something missing. David could not hide the disappointment he felt at having so few sons and the more manly interests which sons would have had, and which he might have shared. In later years he taught his daughters the skills of a surveyor, using theodolites and araeroid barometers to map and contour the heights of Muswell Hill. Indeed, David's training was so good that after his death his youngest daughter Helen was accepted as a tracer in an engineering concern in London on the strength of the work she had done for her father. Later she moved to a post in a department of H.M. Office of Works where she met her future husband Richard Baker, a draughtsman there. Her mapping is excellent still, and she goes on doing research in old maps of Middlesex and Hertfordshire, to prove rights of way for the Ramblers Society.* David also trained his girls as exceptionally neat handwriters and map makers, but he so obviously longed for more boys and these lessons must only have been a disappointing second best. Not that the house was often devoid of young men – Nancy, Betty and Marycita, the older Angus girls, were growing up into exceptionally attractive young ladies, with quite a following of admirers.

Young men must surely have found David quite a daunting person to meet – older than the average father, eccentric, apparently so full of worldly knowledge, even the sheer overwhelming strength of his personality was impressive. Everything about him must have seemed so much larger than life to that generation of innocent youth. But they also liked him, and for all his size or imposing style, he was never *formidable*. So long as they had the sense to listen to his stories and enjoy his constant teasing, most young men were generally welcome. They would find him an easy man to get on with, even

---

*Helen Baker died in November 1988, during the type-setting of this book.

during those awkward moments of silence which young men and fathers sometimes still have to suffer.

A sympathy for women's rights and a shockingly tolerant manner did not, of course, extend to *complete* freedom for the Angus daughters. They were allowed to go 'walking out' but the younger girls were often conscripted as chaperones on visits to Twickenham rugby matches or whatever. Being the father of eight girls cannot have been easy!

In 1912, however, Betty announced her engagement to Harold Nichols, a bank manager slightly older than she was, whom she had met at a tennis club. Betty was a girl of some determination; despite being only 21, she overwhelmed any protests her father many have ventured, and was soon married. Fortunately David could see that his obstinancy, inherited from his mother, had passed on to his children – resistance to Betty would be a waste of time, if his own personality was any measure of his daughter's. Betty and Harold went to live in North Finchley, and thus began the slow, but inevitable, scattering of the Angus family. David did, however, stipulate that the other girls would not be allowed to marry until they were 23, and none defied him.

By now war with Germany had become a real possibility. The papers were full of diplomatic news and editorials which complained bitterly of the rapidly growing German navy. None of this was a surprise to David, who had experienced the Germans himself in Damaraland. By now the area he had explored was called German South West Africa and the tribes there had been harshly subdued. But this was just one example; in Chile too there had been a steadily growing German presence around Coronel. Some towns were almost entirely German in population, to such an extent that David wrote about it to Sir Edward Grey, the British Foreign Secretary. One letter described Coronel itself as a 'hotbed of German intrigue'. Letters from friends in Chile continued to warn of growing German influence and increasing anti-British feeling. David also warned the Foreign Office in the years before the war, that when he went to Germany to inspect railway equipment for South America, he could see stocks of arms piling up everywhere in the steel works and railway marshalling yards. To him it was obvious that war with Germany was coming.

The conflict began in August 1914 and was greeted by most

British people with cheers and songs. Now at last Kaiser Bill would be taught a lesson, seemed to be the popular feeling in a nation with no idea of what was to come. Even in that first month recruiting posters with pictures of Lord Kitchener and his pointing finger began to appear all over the country, and soon a generation of young men were eagerly queuing up to join the army; 500,000 volunteered in August alone.

By now Stewart Angus had graduated from Edinburgh University and, leaving the Stevensons in 1912, he had set off for South America to follow in his father's footsteps. A letter of July 3rd, 1914 shows him to have been working happily as an engineer on the construction staff of the Buenos Aires and Great Southern Railway, at a place called Olavarria. It took time for news of the war to reach South America, especially to the more remote places, but when it did there was not the same wild jingoistic enthusiasm and Stewart did not find himself being swept along in that emotional flood which poured through every British town and village.

It was different for Archie. He was 17 years old and still at school when war broke out. He was pipe major in the Edinburgh Academy pipe band of the Officer Training Corps, and that summer had just won a trophy for piping at Barry OTC camp near Carnoustie. In August he was back in London, full of youthful enthusiasm for the cadets (just as his father had once been for the Volunteers), and sharing David's outrage at the German invasion of Belgium. All around him were examples of people enlisting and one day Archie did the same. The first David knew was when his son announced he had joined the London Scottish regiment as a piper. He soon realised also that as an officer cadet Archie could be shipped to France immediately, without much more training, but Archie calmed him by explaining that the regiment knew of his age and had promised him home duties until he was 18. For a week or so he proudly led recruiting parades through London, but then came a move to Aldershot. Soon after that came Archie's orders for France – easily done in the haste and confusion of so many volunteers – and he was posted to the regiment's second battalion. When David heard of this he protested strongly and was eventually promised that Archie would not travel with the battalion.

The rest of the story is easily told. One morning the Commanding Officer announced on parade that 'Private Angus can go home if he likes'. Archie did not accept the invitation and soon after left with the battalion for France. 'What would you expect me to do?' he wrote later to his father, echoing the words of many young recruits that year. Archie was killed piping the charge of the London Scottish at Messines Ridge on October 31st, 1914.

The news had a shattering effect on David and Mary, from which they never really recovered. For a time their son was listed only as missing and for months they endured the misery of false hope and uncertainty. Enquiries at the War Office could neither confirm nor deny rumours that Archie was prisoner of the Germans. In desperation David wrote to friends in Coronel, requesting them to ask among the more influential Germans if they could find out anything, but this produced no news either. One day news came that a private Archie Angus was among the wounded brought from France to Victoria Station – full of joy the family rushed down to meet him, only to discover a complete stranger with the same name, staring with bewildered sadness at their disappointed faces. Mary especially refused to believe her son was dead but it only made the slow relentless burden of proof all the more painful.

Archie was posted missing on November 1st, the day after the battalion's charge. By a coincidence, on the other side of the world on that same fateful day a German battle fleet destroyed the ships of Admiral Cradock in Coronel Bay, inflicting the first British naval defeat in over a century. That night officers from the victorious German ships came ashore at Coronel and dined in the Angus house – bitter news when it eventually reached David, but proof indeed that Coronel had become a town of German ex-patriates ready to cheer the Kaiser.

When Stewart heard the news of Archie's death he quickly left Argentina for home. Then he too volunteered, and helped to raise a company of Royal Engineers at Edinburgh. He also became engaged to a girl called Kathleen Kerr whom he had earlier met at university – they planned to be married during Stewart's embarkation leave in 1915, but of all things she had German measles and they were not even allowed to meet. Then the regiment sailed to Egypt, from where Stewart's battalion was re-directed to France in 1916. That was the summer of the great push on the River Somme, when Lord Kitchener's new army of keen recruits was slaughtered in the worst killing ever suffered by the British Army. On July 1st, the first day of the battle, Stewart was killed at Hebuterne, cutting barbed wire to allow others through to that hopeless attack. Twenty thousand more British soldiers were killed on that first day, most, like Stewart, in the first few minutes of the offensive.

The tragic loss of the Anguses' last son was no worse than that suffered by thousands of other British families, but that did not make it any less painful to the family. It was a terrible time, from which David especially never recovered his pre-war genial nature. After 1916 there always seemed to be a sadness hiding behind even his happiest moments. But the family rallied – despite the anguish of war, or perhaps because of it, they rolled up their sleeves and supported Britain more than ever.

Nineteen year old Jean became a VAD, went to France and met her future husband Norman Tatham while working in a hospital at Trouville. Joy enlisted in the Land Army on her 17th birthday and finished up doing forestry work on Ben Nevis. Nancy left a secretarial job and became a VAD, and Marycita joined the government's censorship department. In 1917 Betty's husband Harold Nichols was drowned when his troopship was torpedoed in the Mediterranean. She promptly learned to drive and became a volunteer ambulance driver in Kent where she eventually met Oliver Moon, a Canadian Captain in the Medical Corps. They married in 1919, both in uniform, and later settled in Vancouver.

There is a nice story about Marycita. In 1916 she became engaged to William Scott Stevenson, whom she had first met as an art student while he was at Edinburgh University. Now he was a major and they were married during a short leave in 1917, but it was all so hurried that there was no time to find a house and she remained with her family when he returned to France. One day Marycita was drawing a picture of a memorial in the crypt of St. Paul's cathedral, working on an order for some charity. Tears were running down her cheeks when a little old man appeared and asked what was the matter. She told him that her husband was on the front, but they had no house so that when he came home on spells of short leave they had nowhere private to go, just the house at Muswell Hill full of sisters. The old man turned out to be the Archdeacon of St. Paul's and he found her a tiny flat in Grey's Inn at the top of a building full of lawyers' chambers. William and Mary got their house after all, and in the meantime it became a place for Marycita's younger sisters to visit whenever they had a chance. William also survived the war, and later they emigrated to Australia.

So much for the war and the Angus girls. David himself became a Special Constable, helping to guard the local water works and other essential installations. He and Mary also joined the Spanish and Portuguese sections of the government's censorship department as translators and examiners, offering what skills they could at their more advanced age. At the end of each day they were able to travel home together – a small pleasure amidst their sad memories of the war.

In 1917 David was also asked to travel with a number of other engineers to Serbia (now in Yugoslavia) where an Allied advance was expected to liberate that country from Austrian occupation. It was assumed that the railway system there would be in a mess after years of warfare and that experts would be needed to assess damage quickly and get it functioning again, to help further Allied attacks into Austria. David and the other engineers on standby even grew beards before posting, for they were told that the Serbians had no use for beardless men! In the end, however, the Allied advance failed and Serbia remained in Austrian hands until almost the end of the war. When it was finally liberated there was no longer any urgency about repairing the railway system and David was never sent to Serbia.

In addition to the family's various contributions to the war effort, the Anguses also threw open their house to soldiers home on leave. By now there were Wilsons and Anguses all over the Empire, and all seem to have given the Muswell Hill address to any men they knew who were going off to fight in France. Even Nurse tipped off her nephews in Canada. As a result, complete strangers would often turn up at the house – sometimes a score or more if a convoy ship had just reached the Thames from Australia or New Zealand. It reminded Mary of the young engineers who had so often visited the various Angus houses in

South America, filling them with laughter and conversation and pipe tobacco smoke. Now these Anzac invasions became so frequent that she developed a routine of baking a large flat apple tart and a mountain of scones each week, just in case. Then when these and the bread ran out the soldiers made dampers with flour in the kitchen. Lots of them fell in love with Jean or Joy when the girls were at home, and asked to meet them again. Sometimes the younger girls had to be sent to various rendezvous with messages that Jean or Joy could not come. Mostly, however, it was the young men who never came back to London. 'It was a bloody war, and we children grew up with a perpetual sense of men going to their deaths,' wrote Peggy in later years.

In the end the Anguses were a typical British family at war. Two sons and a husband were killed. That vision of David Angus and Sons, Civil Engineers, was gone too. There were urgent wartime marriages, grieving fiancees, and uncomprehending little children. Older, more serious girls volunteered to do their bit while parents with senses dulled counted the days to that eruption of joy in November 1918 when the ceasefire began. It was a story of loss and devotion and stoical courage repeated in homes all over the country.

When it was all over, however, it became clear that the war had also destroyed the Anguses' hopes and fortunes. Their entire standard of life changed; quite a few South American railways had failed during the war, or had at least stopped paying dividends, and David's income fell considerably. In addition, the censorship office gave notice at the end of the war to employees over 60. David was 63, and prospects of work for a man of his age were poor in a world of shattered economies and stagnant trade. What work there was would rightly go to young men home from the war – older men like David were thought of as retired and would have to wait, for they had enjoyed something of life already. As sources of income disappeared, life changed; from 1916 to 1926, for example, Louie never once received new clothing, except a uniform from the school – otherwise only hand-me-downs from her sisters. From now on the Angus family was quite simply, poor. It was not easy for the Anguses to face their new circumstances but David accepted the situation philosophically, as he had done all the other ups and downs he and Mary had shared. Only this time there was none of the optimism he had shown in the past. The loss of Stewart and Archie had knocked the heart out of him and he never regained that cocky Angus confidence.

Each day there was still a journey to the office, but the world recovered slowly from the war and new engineering work was scarce. Soon David and Mary were forced to find additional ways of making money. One was by translating Spanish or Portuguese articles, or typing theses and even novels in Spanish for students at the School for Oriental and African Studies – Mary even had special letters and accents added to her typewriter for this. Mary also got a large knitting machine and ran her own little postal and neighbourhood business, making knitted suits and jerseys and baby clothes. It was hard work, and only just paid.

After the war Nancy, the oldest daughter, worked in France for the American Graves Registration Department. This was a well paid job and with her income she paid for her younger sisters Peggy and Helen to attend the North London Collegiate School. When the graves work ended Nancy returned to London and got a job on the administration of the School for Oriental and African Studies, which allowed her sisters to continue their schooling. Being the oldest child perhaps gave Nancy feelings of responsibility which the others did not sense; while they married and moved on, she stayed to look after the others in the family and in the end she never married.

In 1919 there arrived the family of David's brother George from South Africa. He had never recovered from a head wound during the Boer War and family life was now more trying. As a result his wife and four daughters came to stay with David until 1921. George, although promising that he would follow them, never did and died later. They were given a part of the house including a kitchenette, but the two families often mixed. The four daughters were the same age as David's youngest four and they became great friends together. (In 1914 David's elderly aunt Anne Stewart, from Dundee, came south also with the idea of living with the family, but just a week of noisy children and bustling activity persuarded her to move instead to Tunbridge Wells, where she lived to her death, supported by David and his two American brothers James and William.)

Despite their reduced circumstances, David still led as full a life as ever. There were friends in various walks of life – Conan Doyle, Charles Challen and many more – and there were favourite books on Scottish history. Golf dwindled away after 1914 but there was still chess and gardening, and a little whist. David also had a keen interest in scientific developments, more than just an enthusiasm for his profession. He had a special respect for Lord Kelvin, a pioneer of thermodynamics and electricity, and a picture of a memorial window to Lord Kelvin hung in David's study.

Life may still have been active and David's brain still sharp and alert, but engineering projects were just not there to be worked on. There were quite a few tenders for railways and other works, usually in Chile and Brazil, but most were unsuccessful in the face of cheaper American and even German competition. It was not a completely dismal picture however. In 1920 Jean went out to marry Norman Tatham in South Africa and thereafter a correspondence began with London. This shows that David was at least working on plans for bridges both in Brazil and Montevideo. By February 1921 work was also progressing on railways in Bolivia and Chile which David had designed for the Railway and Works Company. By May at least one more line was under way in Chile, to the town of Valagante, and a hopeful tender had been submitted for the Casa Blanca line from Valparaiso to Santiago. It gives an impression of considerable activity, but it was fitful work and David made little money out of it.

The only project which David is known to have been working on in Britain was for a scheme called 'road-rails'. This involved fitting caterpillar tracks to special small but strong locomotives to be used on rails in hilly country. Each locomotive had an external set of wheels with a set of tracks like a bulldozer. During the 1924 British Empire Exhibition at Wembley a special hilly track was built all round the grounds and these trains ran about demonstrating their abilities to overseas visitors. The exhibition was so successful that it continued on into 1925 but no record survives in the Angus family to show if David made much money out of 'road-rails'. In any case that year he was diverted by something much closer to his heart.

That year what seemed to be *the* miracle happened. David was approached about going back to Brazil, to a district on the border called the Triangulos Mineros which he had surveyed as a speculation while working in Brazil in 1882 and again from the Paraguayan side in 1890. At that time he said he had found every known metal there, and some more which he did not know, but events had prevented him from developing his finds. Now in his twilight years the chance had come for him to return to Brazil, where his life in South America had begun. Of course at the age of 70 he could no longer rough it as he had done 40 years earlier, but he was to go as leader and advisor of a group of younger engineers who would survey for him.

It was the chance he had been waiting for since 1909. The children were old enough to be left alone now (the youngest was 18) and he and Mary could travel out to South America by themselves. For the first time since the war David was filled with hope again. During the rest of 1925 he worked on details of the project and for those months the house was busy with talk and plans for the return to Brazil. In the first week of 1926 he caught a severe cold but still the plans went on eagerly. From his bed David organised a drawing office in the dining room, where Peggy and Louie and Helen spent hours tracing and re-drawing maps and typing out notes. As Peggy wrote later, 'he was on the crest of a wave'. Every so often the girls went upstairs with their work and sat on the bed while their father corrected it and affectionately called them his 'wooden headed objects'. But then the cold turned to pneumonia, a killer in the days before antibiotics. For a time David seemed to be holding his own, but he died quite suddenly just after midnight on Saturday 10th January.

David was buried at the Marylebone Cemetery in Finchley, in a funeral attended, it is said, by someone from every job he had ever done in the past – people with names like Lumsden and Coakes and Fairlie and others from works all over South America who had seen the announcement in the papers. He was lowered into the ground by relatives in the Scottish custom, which irritated the local undertakers who were unused to such change and did not understand his intense Scottishness, nor the bond he shared with his family. In another break with tradition Mary attended the graveside, as if to stay with David to the last as much as she had loved him and been happy with him all through life.

To the family it was a blessing that the Brazilian work had

come when it did, for David died a happy man. They feared that the survey organisers were wanting only to pick his brain, to use his expertise and then find some excuse to leave him behind when the time came, but he died before that possibility could ever happen.

In some ways David was a naive man whose belief in virtues like honesty and kindness were too simple in a changing world. An old colleague said of him when he died: 'He was the straightest man I ever knew, and the most generous minded to all, incapable of meanness in thought or action of any kind.' David also made mistakes, especially in leaving Chile without having another job ready to move into, but what sticks in the mind most is that it was too easy to take advantage of his nature, too easy to hurt him. His daughter Louie recently wrote in a letter:

'When I learnt Kipling's "If" I thought of David Angus and still do. Today the destroyers of faith have made people embarassed by such poems and laugh at standards – one is shy of making such claims, but for all the scoffers laughing at so-called Victorian hypocrisy and double-standards – these were but occasional excrescences on the real true standards which thousands of Victorian men and women upheld throughout the Empire and the world beyond – duty and honesty.'

In her later life people used to sympathise with Mary, for she faced considerable poverty as a widow, but she once answered her children by telling them firmly 'none of you will ever have such a wonderful life as I had'. Mary died in 1939 and lies buried with David. The names of Archie and Stewart are also carved on the headstone, with the dates when they fell in action. Nancy, who never married but devoted her life to the others in the family, has her name on the stone, and so has Nurse, who was interred with the family she made her own.

In 1926 it was still common for families to chose a verse for mourning cards. They chose lines from Browning for David, and they are indeed a fitting epitaph:

One who never turned his back but marched breast forward,
Never doubted clouds would break,
Never dreamed, though right were worsted, wrong would
   triumph,
Held we fall to rise, are baffled to fight better,
Sleep to wake.

Index